PREHISTORIC ANIMALS

A
GROSSET
ALL-COLOR GUIDE

PREHISTORIC ANIMALS

BY BARRY COX

Illustrated by Design Practitioners, Ltd.

Supervising Editor . . . . Georg Zappler

Board of Consultants

Richard G. Van Gelder . . . . Chairman and Curator, Mammals,
American Museum of Natural History

William C. Steere . . . . Director, New York Botanical Gardens

Sune Engelbrektson . . . . Space Science Co-ordinator,
Port Chester Public Schools

John F. Middleton . . . . Chairman, Anthropology,
New York University

Carl M. Kortepeter . . . . Associate Professor, History,
New York University

Michael Cohn . . . . Curator, Cultural History,
Brooklyn Children's Museum

Frank X. Critchlow . . . . Consulting Engineer, Applied and
Theoretical Electronics

GROSSET & DUNLAP
A NATIONAL GENERAL COMPANY
Publishers • New York

FOREWORD

This guide tells the story of the vertebrates—that group of animals consisting of fish, amphibians, reptiles, birds and mammals. Because we are ourselves mammals, it is partly out own history that is followed back to an unimaginably distant point in the past—over 400 million years ago.

The study of fossils is known as vertebrate paleontology. Fossils are usually incompletely preserved and are often badly damaged; even their complete skeletons usually give little idea of what they looked like when alive. Vertebrate paleontologists and artists, working together, can reconstruct their original appearance, and such reconstructions have been used throughout this book. Only their colors are pure guesswork.

CONTENTS

INTRODUCTION

Why study fossils?

Many people find the thought of the varied bizarre creatures that have lived on this planet a fascinating one. These creatures included some whose size and weight were far greater than those of any animal now living, and others at whose habits and diet we can only guess. The plants that surrounded them, and even the position and arrangement of the continents and oceans they inhabited, were also very different from those we know today.

The fossils of vertebrates, as animals with backbones are called, are of particular interest for several reasons. They have shown an unsurpassed adaptability, for they have colonized both the waters and the land, and some can even fly. The story of how they did this lies in the rocks under our feet and, despite some gaps, it is fairly complete. Some evolutionary histories, such as the gradual evolution of the horse, a vertebrate, are particularly well understood. Such detailed histories of fossil animals are the most important evidence of the occurrence of evolution that we possess. The realization of this fact has led to rewarding insights into many biological problems, and also gives a rather different view of our own relationship to the rest of the world's living creatures. From this arises another unique interest, for we ourselves are vertebrates, just a small twig of the great evolutionary tree that this book describes.

This mammoth has become trapped in the soft mud around the edge of an Ice Age lake. When the mud dries and hardens, its carcass will be entombed.

4

What is a fossil?

The history of the vertebrates is known in such detail because they have hard bony skeletons. After an animal dies, its soft parts rapidly decay and the bones are usually the only parts that may become fossilized. This will happen only if they become buried in accumulating mud or sand, which will prevent their decay or destruction. Some of the chemicals in the bone may gradually be dissolved away by percolating water, which will deposit others in their place, although this usually does not alter the structure of the bone itself. The surrounding mud or sand may then gradually become compressed and hardened into rock, thus encasing the now fossilized bones and preserving an almost permanent record of the animal.

Sometimes the bone is later dissolved away completely, leaving its shape as a cavity or mold within the rock. Very rarely, the impression of such soft structures as fins or feathers may be preserved. Other relics of vertebrate history include their footprints, made in mud that has later dried and which have been hardened, and the remains of the shells of the eggs of fossil reptiles.

Several millions of years later, erosion of the earth's surface has exposed the fossilized bones of the mammoth.

How fossils are collected and studied

A paleontologist does not search haphazardly nor, usually, does he dig to find fossils. He will first decide what he wants to find and, after examining the results of reconnaissances or detailed geological studies, he might decide that suitable rocks were most plentiful in central Africa or South America. An expedition to collect fossils in such a place may take several months of preparation and cost a considerable amount.

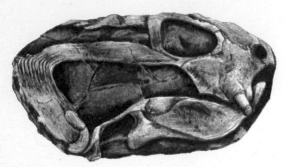

The outer parts of a reptile skull, six inches long and over 200 million years old, can be seen at the surface of the nodule.

Once the paleontologist has arrived in a chosen area, he will search for cliffs, the banks of streams or other places where the rocks are being eroded by the weather. He will collect fossils thus exposed and only dig into the rock to free those still partially embedded.

A fossil may be enclosed in a lump of hard rock, or 'nodule', that can immediately be packed up to take away. Very often, however, the bones are broken, or many may be lying together and, in these cases, the paleontologist carefully clears away any loose earth or rock. Then, after putting a thin layer of soft wetted paper over the exposed surface of the fossil he protects it with strips of sacking soaked in plaster of Paris. If the fossil is partially embedded in the rock, it is removed by digging around and under it. When it can be safely turned over, its newly freed surface is protected in the same way. If the skeleton is large it may be necessary to divide it into pieces and treat each piece in this way. The resulting blocks may be quite bulky and heavy and must be carefully packed into boxes for transport back to the laboratory. The paleontologist will also give a 'field number' to each specimen, and record exactly where it was found.

In the laboratory the plaster of Paris is removed and then much, or all, of the rock surrounding the bones is also removed using a variety of chemical or mechanical methods. When no more rock can be removed, the paleontologist can begin to study the bones. He will use his knowledge of other related animals, especially any still living, and attempt to reconstruct the appearance, diet and habits of the long-dead creature.

The skeleton of the fossil is cleared of loose earth, and then it is protected with wetted paper and plaster of Paris. The bones are freed from the rock in the laboratory.

How evolution changes animals

In many cases the fossils from successive rock layers show gradual changes in their structure. Although these series may give very strong evidence that evolution has taken place, they tell us nothing of the mechanism of evolution. For this we must examine populations of living animals.

It was Darwin who first deduced this mechanism. He pointed out that most animals produce a large number of young. Because the number of animals in the population remains fairly stable, many of these offspring must die before they reach maturity and reproduce in their turn. They must, therefore, be competing with each other in a *struggle for survival*. If they all were identical, the result of this struggle would be quite random, and any pair of animals might survive to take their parents' place in the population. But, as Darwin noticed, the offspring of a single pair of adults are not identical. They show, instead, slight variations in their structure or capabilities. Those that possess a variation that gives them a slight advantage, perhaps in speed or stamina, over their competitors in their generation will ultimately survive to reproduce. Their offspring may, in turn, possess this advantageous variation and be able to compete successfully, so that the new characteristic gradually spreads through the population in succeeding generations.

Evolutionary changes usually take place too slowly to be noticeable within a human lifetime, but the pepper-moth of northern England makes an interesting exception to this rule. This moth is colored to merge with the bark of the trees on which it lives, and so it escapes detection by its predators. During the early nineteenth century it was a mottled silver-gray color, but there were a few darker moths in the population. When the trees became darkened with soot during the Industrial Revolution, these darker moths became less noticeable than their lighter-colored relatives. More darker moths survived, and they now form the major part of the pepper-moth population.

Most naturally occurring variations produce only a slight change in the organism. Such continual variations in a species provide it with a flexibility that allows it to remain closely adapted to its gradually changing environment.

The paler, speckled type of pepper-moth cannot be seen on clean, normal bark. The darker type is, similarly, difficult to see on soot-blackened bark. The chart below illustrates the fact that, in the years from 1848 to 1948, the percentage of dark-colored pepper-moths in the population rose from less than 1% to 99%.

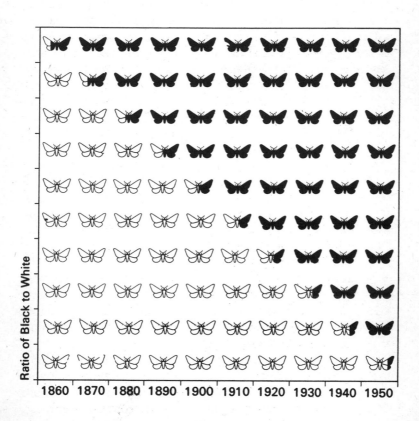

Ratio of Black to White

1860 1870 1880 1890 1900 1910 1920 1930 1940 1950

9

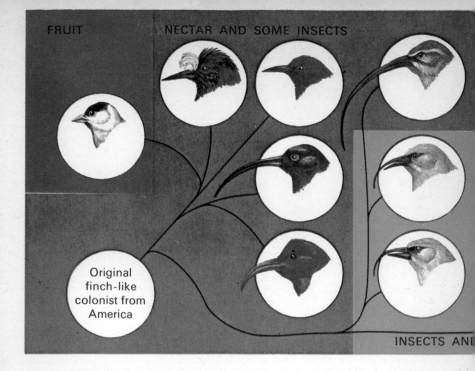

Original finch-like colonist from America

Adaptations

Occasionally the process of natural selection gradually produces a set of characteristics that opens a wide range of new opportunities to its possessor. An example of this is the evolution of wings and feathers in a group of reptiles that lived about 150 million years ago. These first warm-blooded flying vertebrates, the birds, found that there were very many different ways in which their resulting power of sustained flight could be used. Gradually a whole *adaptive radiation* of birds evolved, occupying every way of life possible for a flying vertebrate, from the tiny humming-bird to the giant eagle. Some, like the ostrich, have even lost the power of flight and, instead, use their powerful hind legs for fast movement and for defense. Each of these different types of bird shows adaptations to its particular way of life. The most obvious of these adaptations are usually modi-fications, or specializations, of the the shape of its feet, beak and wings, structures involving locomotion and feeding.

In such an adaptive radiation, the earliest member is often spoken of as 'primitive', in that it may not yet have developed

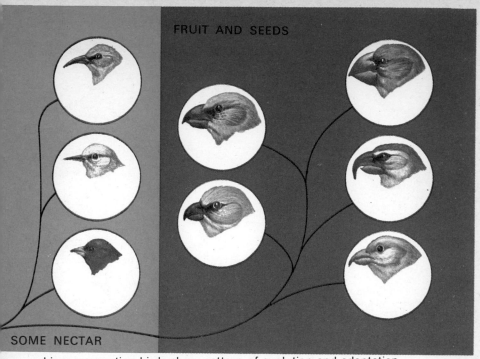

SOME NECTAR

Lines connecting birds show pattern of evolution and adaptation.

all the features that characterize later members of the group. For example, the earliest bird had not developed the shortened tail and toothless beak of later birds, which are said to be more 'advanced' in these features. Progressions of this kind, from a primitive to an advanced condition, can be seen particularly well on a large scale in the bony fish (see page 28) and in the mammal-like reptiles (see page 58).

Striking examples of adaptive radiation on a smaller scale are sometimes found on small isolated islands. Because few animals manage to reach such islands, those which do find little competition. Many ways of life are therefore open to them, and these fortunate immigrants undergo a comparatively rapid adaptive radiation. A well-known example of this occurred on the Hawaiian Islands. This group of Pacific islands lies 2,800 miles from the nearest land. A few little birds known as honey-creepers (see chart above) originally colonized them, and they have since become modified, particularly in the shape of their bills, to a variety of diets, such as fruit, seeds, nuts or insects.

How animals are classified

The way in which a group of animals, such as the vertebrates, radiated into a variety of forms can be compared to the structure of a tree. Just as parts of the tree of different size are given different names, such as trunk, branch, twig and leaf, so a series of names are given to the differently sized groups of animals. In this way all the vertebrates are placed in a single *phylum*, which is divided into a number of *classes*, such as the Amphibia and the Reptilia. Each of these

Animals, such as the vertebrates, radiate into a variety of forms and a series of names are given to the differently sized groups.

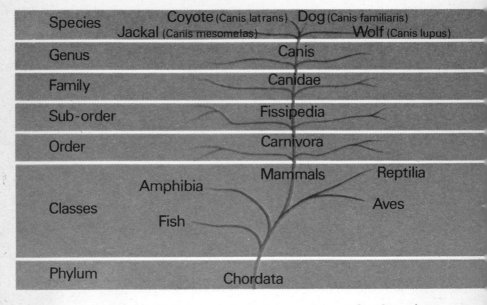

classes is divided successively into *orders, suborders, families, genera* and *species*. For example, dogs, coyotes, wolves and jackals are all different species of the genus *Canis*, which belongs to the family Canidae of the order Carnivora in the class Mammalia.

Most living animals have a common name, such as 'wolf', as well as a scientific name which indicates the genus and species—in this case, *Canis lupus*. There are no common names for extinct animals, and fossils can only be referred to by their scientific name unless, like the saber-toothed tiger or woolly rhinoceros, they are closely related to a living animal.

Sometimes the name of the species can be used to indicate the range or occurrence of an animal, for example *'africanus'*, while other scientific names often derive from the name of a characteristic used in classifying the specimen. For example, the commonest herbivores living about 120 million years ago belonged to a group known as the Dicynodontia; this name means 'two dog-toothed', and refers to the pair of tusk-like canine teeth that are characteristic of this group.

For example, the animal shown above belongs to the phylum Vertebrata because it has a hard bony skull and internal skeleton. It is a member of the class Reptilia because it has a dry imperme-able skin, has limbs not fins and lays hard-shelled eggs. It belongs to the order Lacertilia because its limbs are not reduced like those of snakes, and to the family Chameleontidae because its fingers and toes are bound together into two opposable groups for grip-ping branches. The long tail shows that it belongs to the genus *Chamaeleo,* and the flap of skin behind the head shows that it is a specimen of the species *Chamaeleo dilepis.*

13

EARTH'S HISTORY

The types of rock

The remains of an animal are only likely to be preserved as a fossil if they become buried. This does not usually happen unless they come to lie in the bed of a lake, stream or river, or at the bottom of the sea. Rocks that are formed in such environments are known as sedimentary rocks. They are of several different types, depending on the material that comprised the sediment that was deposited and on the size of the particles.

Very small particles, such as those found in clay, will form a rock known as a shale. A variety of sandstones are formed by the deposition of different types of sand. Both shales and sandstones result from the accumulation of particles that have been brought in from elsewhere, by the action of water and wind eroding the surface of the earth.

Another group of sedimentary rocks includes the limestones and chalks, which are formed differently, by the accumulation of the shells of living creatures. The calcium carbonate of which these shells are composed is absorbed from the water by the animal and laid down in or around the body. Another type of rock is coal, which is formed by

Shales are finely grained rocks. They are usually made up of many very thin layers, along which they can easily be split. Fossils may be compressed between these layers.

Sandstones are more coarsely grained. They do not usually split into layers. Fossils from sandstones are often uncrushed.

Limestones are fine-grained, often pale in color. Their fossils are often very well-preserved and uncrushed.

Coal is an accumulation of partially decomposed plant material.

the preservation of the accumulated remains of plants.

After bones have been buried and fossilized, other layers of rock may form over them. Some of these may be other sedimentary rocks. The molten deeper layers below the Earth's crust may also be forced upward and intrude into these layers as granite or cover the surface as lava. The heat from these 'igneous' rocks will alter, or *metamorphose,* the surrounding rocks, and any fossils in these rocks will usually be destroyed.

The formation of any sedimentary or igneous rock is a fairly local occurrence, usually restricted to a few hundred square miles (although some areas cover several thousand square miles). Each is therefore given a separate name, which is often taken from the area in which it is found, for example the 'Oxford Clay' and the 'London Clay'.

Section showing different types of rock, including metamorphism.

The order of the rocks

Sedimentary rocks always form on the earth's surface. They are therefore always deposited above any earlier, older rocks. Movements in the earth's outer skin or 'crust', may cause some areas to sink down below, or to rise above, neighboring areas, so that these areas will be separated from them by an abrupt change in the rocks.

These changes, or 'faults', may result from a drop of only a few feet, or of several hundred feet. These movements may also fold or crumple the layers of rock, raising them into hills or mountains, and the process of erosion will then start to wear them away and reveal their structure and fossils. All these changes may have obscured the original simple picture, that 'deeper means older', but the geologist can usually work out what has happened, as long as he can follow a particular set of rock layers, or 'strata', from one place to another, and this information can be provided only by the fossils which the rocks contain.

Some types of fossil are found only in older rocks, others only in more recent rocks. Some forms persisted for long stretches of geological time but underwent gradual changes in structure which we now know in considerable detail. As a result of this knowledge, it is usually possible, after an examination of the fossils from a particular stratum of rocks, to define the time in the earth's history when those rocks were, in fact, deposited.

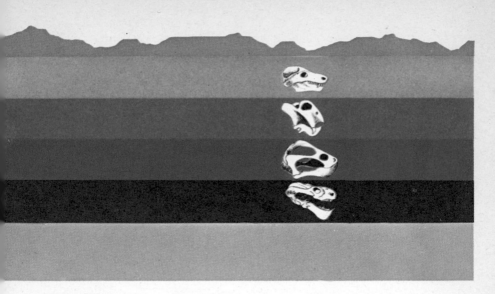

The different layers of rock shown above were laid down in turn, and each contains a different type of reptilian fossil. The rock strata shown below have been distorted and eroded, and the section on the right has dropped below that on the left as the result of a fault.

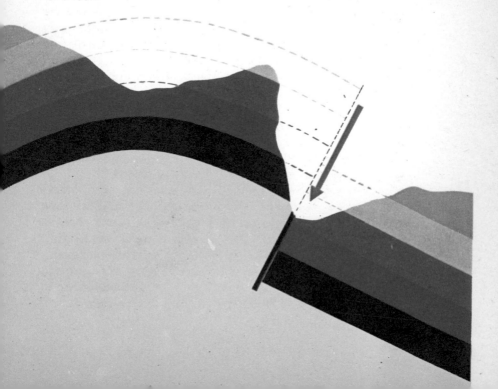

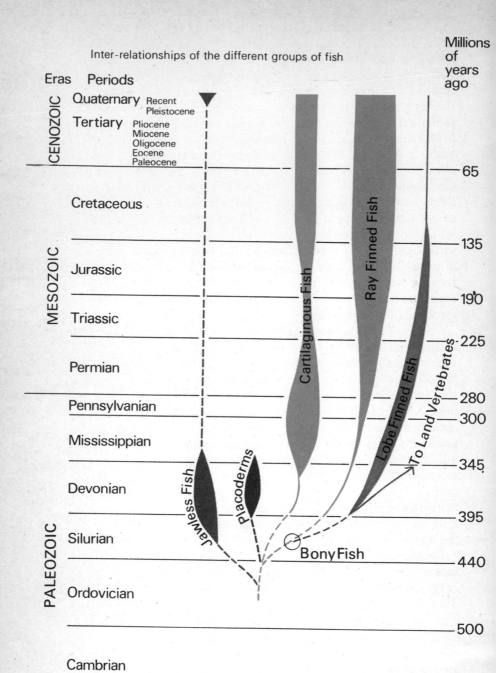

Inter-relationships of the different groups of fish

Dividing up earth's history

Just as it is convenient to divide a big encyclopedia into a number of separate volumes, so it is convenient to divide up the long span of the earth's history. Divisions were first established by giving a name to a group of rocks which were found in a single area and which were similar in their composition and fossils. For example, the rocks which include the chalk deposits of southeastern England were called the Cretaceous Series. The period in the earth's history when these rocks were formed was, similarly, named the Cretaceous period. Any rocks, found anywhere in the world, whose fossils showed that they had been deposited at the same time as the Cretaceous rocks of England, are therefore now said to have been deposited in the Cretaceous period. In this way the history of the fossil-bearing sedimentary rocks has been divided into twelve periods, which have been grouped into three eras.

Dating the rocks

After establishing the order in which all these rocks were formed and grouping them into convenient, named units, the final step is to find out exactly when they were deposited. A variety of methods now rely upon the fact that some rocks contain radioactive elements. These are unstable and gradually disintegrate, forming stable elements. The rate at which this takes place is constant and can be measured. For example, one gram of radioactive uranium forms 1/7000 of a gram of lead in a million years. By measuring the ratio of lead to unchanged uranium, it is possible to calculate for how long the uranium has been disintegrating. This result gives the age of the rock that contained the radioactive mineral.

Measurements of this kind, using minerals containing radioactive forms of uranium, thorium, potassium or carbon, have made it possible to calculate the ages of many rocks. The results are given in the chart on the opposite page. The Cambrian period began about 600 million years ago, and even older, 'Precambrian', rocks are known. These contain few recognizable fossils, but remains that may be fossil algae are known in rocks about 2,500 million years old. The oldest Precambrian rocks were formed about 3,500 million years ago, while the Earth is about 5,000 million years old.

The moving continents

Geologists have long realized that the rocks themselves are not constant, but are continually being eroded away or raised into new mountain ranges. It is only in this century, however, that it has been generally realized that the positions and relationships of the continents have not always been as we see them today.

Similarities between the sequence of rocks in South America and Africa, and between the shapes of their Atlantic coastlines, first suggested that these continents might once have been joined to one another. It was later realized that the early floras of these two continents were similar and that these floras were also found in India, Australia and Antarctica. It was therefore suggested that these five land masses were originally all joined together in a single supercontinent, called Gondwanaland.

North America and Eurasia were thought to have been joined together in a second supercontinent, Laurasia. The two supercontinents were partially separated by a stretch of ocean, the Tethys Ocean.

New lines of research have given support to these ideas and provided more detail. Research using computers has shown that it is possible to fit North and South America very accurately against Europe and Africa. A great ridge that runs down the middle of the North and South Atlantic may mark the line of their original parting, the continents having moved eastward and westward from this ridge.

Another line of research investigates the particles of magnetized iron minerals that became trapped in some igneous rocks as these were formed. As the rocks cooled, the direction of the magnetization of these particles became aligned with the earth's magnetic field and pointed toward the earth's magnetic poles. If the continents have never moved, all these 'fossil magnets' should still be pointing to these poles—but they do not. Instead, they indicate that our continents have scattered to their present positions and did once form a Gondwanaland mass centered around the South Pole and a Laurasian mass farther north.

The continents may originally have been joined in the pattern shown.

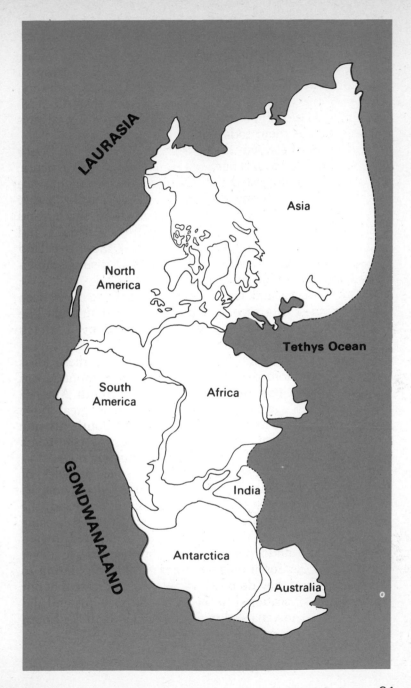

THE HISTORY OF THE VERTEBRATES

Where the vertebrates came from

The vertebrates are a clearly recognizable group of animals, and include the fishes, amphibians, reptiles, birds and mammals. They all have a vertebral column that encloses their spinal nerve cord and (at least at some stage of their life history) gill slits which pierce the body wall in the head region. Which animals they evolved from is less obvious, but the first clue comes from their own development. Their hard vertebral column forms around a softer rod called the *notochord.*

A notochord and gill slits are also found in a little fish-like marine creature called *Amphioxus.* The gills of *Amphioxus* are very numerous and fine and are covered by a protective layer of the body. Such protected gills are also present in the sea squirts, which live attached to rocks in the sea. Although the adult sea squirt does not possess a notochord, or a nerve cord, both are found in its larva, which swims actively until it attaches itself to a rock.

The diagram of the 4 ins. long sea squirt (*left*) shows the water currents through the small gill slits. The larva (*above*) is microscopic.

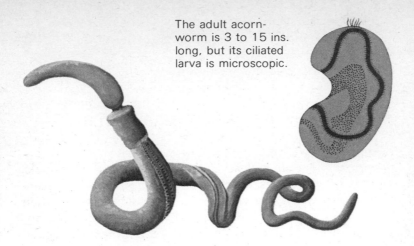

The adult acorn-
worm is 3 to 15 ins.
long, but its ciliated
larva is microscopic.

Gill slits are again found in the acorn-worms, which burrow in sea mud. Their life history gives a final clue to the origins of the vertebrates. Their larvae swim by means of bands of tiny whip-like hairs called 'cilia', and they are microscopic in size.

Very similar larvae are also found in the echinoderms, a group of animals which includes starfish, sea urchins and sea cucumbers. Of all the invertebrates, these slow-moving marine creatures may therefore be the most closely related to ourselves.

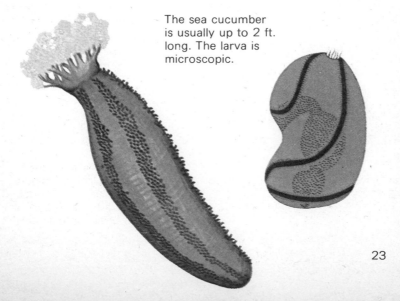

The sea cucumber
is usually up to 2 ft.
long. The larva is
microscopic.

23

Jawless fish

The earliest known vertebrates, the ostracoderms, had not evolved the bony jaws or the pairs of fins that all later fish possess. Unquestionable remains are first found in the Silurian, but they are common only during the Devonian. Some lived in the sea, others in fresh water. Most of them had a heavy jacket of bone around their head and the front part of their body, and thick bony scales over the rest of the body. Some little ostracoderms, such as *Thelodus*, were covered by tiny scales. These 'coelolepids' may be the young of other ostracoderms, rather than being a separate group.

The ostracoderms cannot have been very active and one

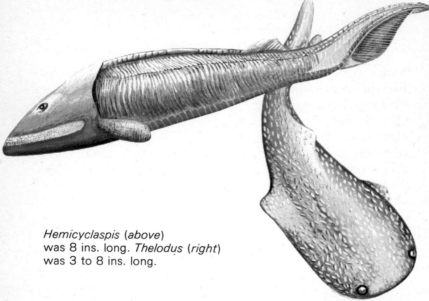

Hemicyclaspis (*above*)
was 8 ins. long. *Thelodus* (*right*)
was 3 to 8 ins. long.

group, the cephalaspids, seem to have lived lying on the bottom and feeding on the mud. Their head-shield is flattened, and the gills open on the underneath or 'ventral' surface. Some parts of the head-shield were covered by a mosaic of tiny bones. The function of these areas is still unknown, but they were probably used to detect vibrations in the water. A few cephalaspids, such as *Hemicyclaspis*, had developed fin-flaps on either side of the head. Another group, including *Pteraspis*, were probably more active but lacked paired fins.

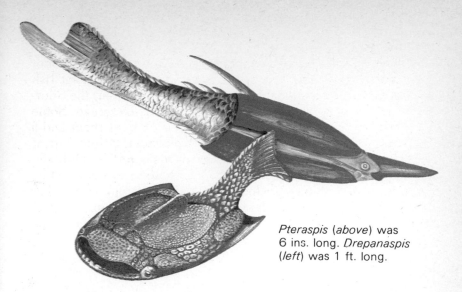

Pteraspis (*above*) was
6 ins. long. *Drepanaspis*
(*left*) was 1 ft. long.

Some, such as *Drepanaspis,* probably lived on the bottom, like the cephalaspids. A final group, the anaspids, such as *Pharyngolepis,* were less heavily armored and more active. One of them had a basket-like arrangement of supporting elements around its gills. This suggests that the anaspids were the ancestors of the living jawless fish, the parasitic cyclostomes, which also have such a gill-basket. The lamprey, *Petromyzon,* and the hag-fishes are the only members of this group.

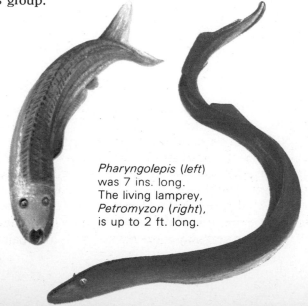

Pharyngolepis (*left*)
was 7 ins. long.
The living lamprey,
Petromyzon (*right*),
is up to 2 ft. long.

25

Dinichthys was
up to 30 ft. long.

Bothriolepis was 1 ft. long.

Climatius was
only 3 ins. long.

Acanthodes was 1 ft. long.

Placoderms

At the same time as the ostracoderms, there lived three
groups of placoderms, fish which had evolved proper jaws
and paired fins. Most fish have two sets of paired fins, a front
or pectoral pair and a rear or pelvic pair.

Two groups of placoderms, the antiarchs and the arthrodires, had heavy armor over the head and front part of the
body. The antiarchs, such as *Bothriolepis,* were flattened
and probably lived on the bottom. Their pectoral append-
ages were enclosed in a jointed bony armor, forming
flippers that must have been used rather like the legs of a
lobster.

The arthrodires were armored only in the head region and
also lacked body scales. Later arthrodires, such as *Coccosteus*
of the Upper Devonian, were quite fast-swimming fish.
Others, such as *Dinichthys,* were up to 30 feet long and
had jaws powerful enough to crack open the armor of ostracoderms or other placoderms. The arthrodires may be related
to the cartilaginous fish (see illustration on opposite page).

The third group, the acanthodians, consisted of unarmored fast-swimming fish. They had quite large fins, with
a spine at the front edge of each. Some, such as *Climatius,*
had seven sets of paired fins. *Acanthodes* survived until the
Lower Permian, longer than any other placoderm. The
acanthodians may be related to the higher bony fish.

26

Cartilaginous fish

The skeleton of the sharks, rays and their relatives is unique, because it is not made of bone, but of a softer substance called cartilage. The only hard parts are the teeth and fin spines, so their fossil history is poorly known, although an early shark, *Cladoselache,* is known from the Upper Devonian.

Nearly all the cartilaginous fish have lived in the sea. From the Mesozoic onward there have been two main lines of development. The best known are the active, usually carnivorous, streamlined sharks and dogfish. Another line, far less active and often living on the bottom, includes the rays and skates. These flattened fish swim by means of their very large pectoral fins and often eat mollusks.

Another minor group, which also eat mollusks, are the chimaeroids. These weird deep-sea fish have a pointed snout and a whip-like tail. They may not be closely related to the other cartilaginous fish, but it seems likely that·all originated from the arthrodires.

Cladoselache (*above*) was 2 to 4 ft. long. Mantas, such as that shown below, are up to 20 ft. long, but chimaeroids (*bottom*) are only about 2 ft. long.

Bony fish – the ray fins

Nearly all the bony fish in the seas and rivers belong to this group, called the Actinopterygii. Their great success is due mainly to their highly perfected methods of swimming and food gathering. The evolution of these characteristics was gradual, but three basic stages can be distinguished—the chondrostean, holostean and teleostean types of fish. Although most of the first two groups are extinct, a few members of each have survived in the fresh water, where competition is less fierce than in the sea. From these survivors we know the anatomy of the soft, fleshy parts of these groups.

The chondrosteans, such as *Cheirolepis,* are known first in the Middle Devonian. They had thick scales and their fins were quite solidly built. Like many other early bony fish, they had a lung. One factor in their success lay in the gradual transformation of this lung into an air-bladder. By regulating the amount of air in this bladder, the fish can give its body the same density as the surrounding water. It can then hang motionless in the water and does not have to use energy to prevent itself from sinking to the bottom or rising to the surface. The gradual evolution of such a swim-bladder was accompanied by thinning of the scales and reduction of the fin skeleton. The Mesozoic holosteans, such as *Caturus,* show a stage in these changes intermediate between the chondrosteans and the teleosts.

The other key to the success of the ray-finned fish lay in their jaw mechanism (described opposite). Over half the species of living fish are advanced teleosts of this kind.

The digestive system and silvery air-bladder take up very little space in the body of the teleost, most of which is composed of the powerful swimming musculature.

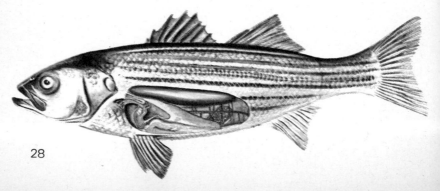

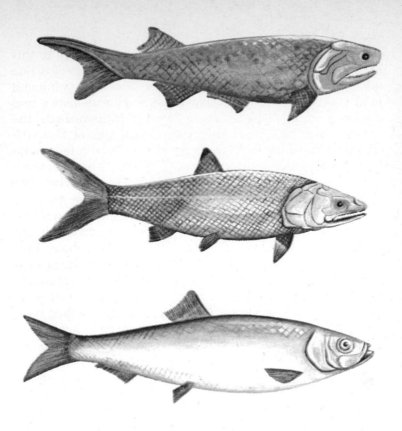

Cheirolepis (*top*) was 9 ins. long. *Caturus* (*middle*) was 2 ft. long. The herring, *Clupea* (*bottom*) is about 8 ins. long. Note the reduction of the fleshy upper lobe of the tail fin. Advanced teleosts (*below*) protrude their jaws toward their prey and simultaneously enlarge the mouth cavity so that water, including the prey, is sucked in.

Bony fish–the lobe-fins

The other branch of bony fish, called the Crossopterygii, has been less successful in the water than the Actinopterygii. From these, however, the land vertebrates evolved. In the crossopterygians, the skeleton and its musculature extends well down into the fin, which therefore looks very solid and fleshy. The three different groups of crossopterygian fish all appear in the Devonian.

The *lungfish* are mollusk-eating fresh-water fish. Only three genera still survive. One, *Neoceratodus* of Australia, breathes mainly through its gills and uses the paired lungs only to obtain extra oxygen if it is very active. Similar fish lived as long ago as the Pennsylvanian. The other two living genera, *Protopterus* of Africa and *Lepidosiren* of South America, have reduced their fins to slender tentacles and have reduced their scales. They can survive dry seasons by burrowing into the mud and forming a cocoon. During this time they use their lungs for obtaining oxygen from the air. Fossil lungfish of this type, and their burrows, are known from the Permian.

Most of the *coelacanths* were marine, with a characteristic

An African lungfish in its cocoon, which opens to the surface by a small hole.

The Australian lungfish *Neoceratodus* (*top*) is about 3 ft. long. The African lungfish *Protopterus* (*bottom*) is about 2 ft. long.

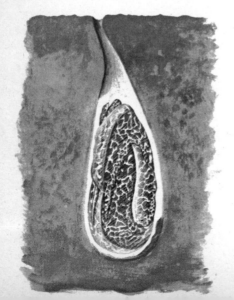

Latimeria is about
5 ft. long.

fin arrangement of dorsal and ventral fin placed just in front
of a large tail fin. They were thought to have died out in the
Cretaceous until one was caught off eastern Africa in 1939.
Several more of this living genus, *Latimeria,* have been
caught since that time.

The *rhipidistians,* such as *Eusthenopteron,* are the most
interesting of the crossopterygians, as they are the most
closely related to the land vertebrates. The skeleton of their
fins is very like that of the early Amphibia, and both groups
have teeth whose enamel covering is folded in toward the
center of the tooth. The rhipidistians were predatory fresh-
water fish, and their extinction in the Lower Permian was
probably partly due to competition from their descendants,
the Amphibia.

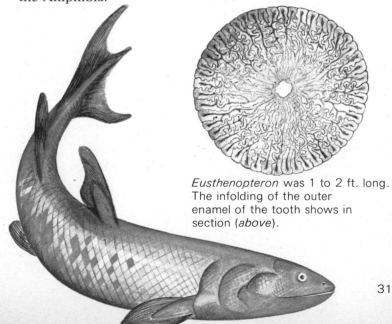

Eusthenopteron was 1 to 2 ft. long.
The infolding of the outer
enamel of the tooth shows in
section (*above*).

31

The skeleton of *Ichthyostega* shows the well-developed limbs and tail-fin.

On to the land

There are many differences between the conditions in water and those on land. The change from one environment to the other was the most difficult of all the achievements of the vertebrates. For example, the weight of an aquatic animal is borne partly by the water, but a land animal must be able to support the whole weight of its body. The fish's paddle-fin therefore, had to be transformed into a more solid pillar-like limb and the fish turned into a four-footed, or 'tetrapod', land animal.

It is not surprising to find that it was the lobe fin of the crossopterygians, rather than the more frail fin of the actinopterygians, which proved capable of this modification of structure. Although the old method of locomotion, using the tail, could not be used on land, many of the early tetrapods still spent much of their time in the water and several, such as *Ichthyostega* and *Archeria,* still had a tail fin.

The rest of the animal's skeleton, too, became adapted to supporting the weight of its body. The vertebral column become more solidly constructed and was attached to the

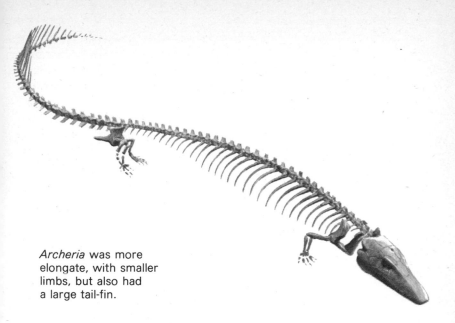

Archeria was more
elongate, with smaller
limbs, but also had
a large tail-fin.

pelvic girdle, with which the hind limbs articulate. The tetrapods also developed an eardrum with which they were able to detect air-borne sounds that have to be amplified to be picked up by the fluid surrounded nerves of the inner ear. The eye had to be protected by eyelids and moistened by tear glands, and its structure adapted to seeing in air instead of in water.

Although the tetrapods now had to obtain their oxygen from air, they would have found little difficulty in this. As we have seen already, their fish ancestors had lungs as well as gills. In the most primitive living tetrapods, the amphibians, the change from gill respiration to lung respiration takes place during the life of each animal. Frog and salamander young still develop in the water and spend their early life there. This may be because suitable food for these little creatures is more readily available in the water. Whatever the reason may be, the young amphibian is wholly aquatic, breathing through gills and swimming by means of a tail. Only later does the familiar tadpole become able to live on land, by growing limbs and using its lungs.

A few names

With their emergence on to the land, the structure of the tetrapods became fairly stable and this is, therefore, a suitable point at which to note the scientific names of a few of their bones. It is, for example, much simpler to refer to the 'radius' instead of the 'inner bone of the lower part of the front limb', and the other bones of the skeleton are named in the same way.

Though the skull in early vertebrates may include about sixty different bones, many of these may be lost or fused together in later forms. The basic structure of the skull is, however, similar. The skull is pierced by holes for the nostrils and eyes, and the eardrums are situated in notches in its rear edge.

Behind the neck, the vertebral column bears long ribs which protect and support the body contents or viscera. The limbs are attached to bony girdles. The pectoral girdle lies outside the ribs. Its upper parts are composed mainly

The skeleton of the Permian amphibian *Seymouria.*

of a pair of shoulder blades or scapulae, as they are called, but its ventral parts meet in the mid-line where a breast bone or sternum develops. The upper part of the pelvic girdle is attached to the strong short ribs of a few special vertebrae, the sacrals. Behind these, the vertebral column continues as a long tail.

In advanced tetrapods the body is poised above straight limbs, so that the bones of these limbs take its weight. But in the early tetrapods the body hangs between the limbs, and large muscles are needed to prevent it from collapsing to the

Limb position of an early
tetrapod (*left*) and advanced
tetrapod (*right*).

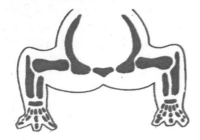
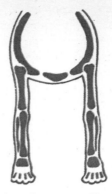

ground. The limb bones must therefore be of a size sufficient to provide large surfaces to which these muscles can be attached.

The upper part of the front limb is composed of a single bone, the humerus, but the lower part contains two bones, an outer ulna and an inner radius. Beyond these lie the little carpal bones that form the wrist region. Each finger is composed of a basal metacarpal bone and a number of phalanges. The hind limb is of a similar construction, containing an upper femur and a lower tibia and fibula, while the foot is made up of tarsals, metatarsals and phalanges.

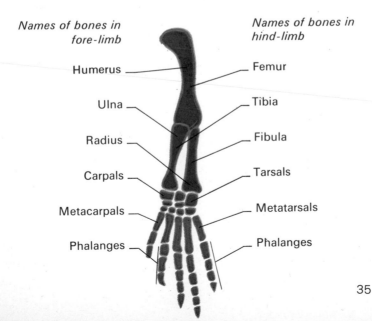

Names of bones in fore-limb

Humerus
Ulna
Radius
Carpals
Metacarpals
Phalanges

Names of bones in hind-limb

Femur
Tibia
Fibula
Tarsals
Metatarsals
Phalanges

35

Why colonize the land?

Because conditions are more variable and difficult on land, one may perhaps wonder why the vertebrates first colonized this awkward environment. There are, however, several possible reasons.

One important reason is likely to be the fact that fresh water is far more temporary than the sea, as many pools and streams disappear in the dry season. Like the living lungfish (see page 30), the fresh-water rhipidistian ancestors of the tetrapods would have been able to use their lungs for respiration during this time. But, unlike the mollusk-eating lungfish, the rhipidistians ate other fish. Most of their prey would have been gill-breathing fish, which would have died when the water became stagnant, some time before it actually dried up.

One suggestion is that the tetrapods first ventured on to the land in order to search for another, larger stretch of water. Here they could once more resume their normal fish-eating life.

There are some difficulties connected with this theory, however. The fish-eating adult rhipidistian would have found no suitable food on its overland journey, and would have found it difficult to drag its large body very far. It seems more likely that it was its young which first ventured onto land.

The young of many of today's fish often go into the shallows to escape from large predatory fish, and the lung-breathing young rhipidistians might well have gone farther, on to the banks. These little, lighter fish would have found progress much easier than the adults, and would, therefore, have been able to feed on the larvae of insects and on riverside invertebrates.

Once the young rhipidistians had evolved into small terrestrial amphibians, they would in their turn have provided suitable food for the larger tetrapods. The fossil record seems to support this theory, for the earliest terrestrial amphibians are the little lepospondyls (see chart on opposite page). None of the larger labyrinthodont amphibians appears to have become fully terrestrial until the Permian.

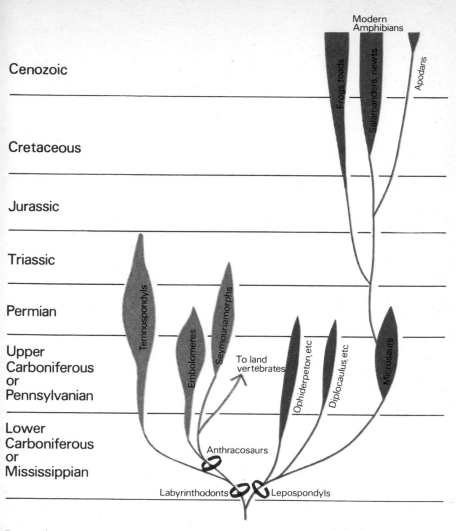

Cenozoic

Cretaceous

Jurassic

Triassic

Permian

Upper
Carboniferous
or
Pennsylvanian

Lower
Carboniferous
or
Mississippian

Devonian

Modern
Amphibians

Frogs, toads

Salamanders, newts

Apodans

Temnospondyls

Embolomeres

Seymouriamorphs

To land
vertebrates

Ophiderpeton, etc

Diplocaulus, etc

Microsaurs

Anthracosaurs

Labyrinthodonts

Lepospondyls

This chart illustrates how, very early in their history, the amphibians split into two separate groups. The labyrinthodonts, to the left, may eventually have given rise to the reptiles. The lepospondyls, indicated on the right, may include the ancestors of the various modern amphibia.

37

The amphibian life history
Although it is usually said that the amphibians conquered the land, only an adult amphibian can, in fact, live on the land, as has been explained on page 33. The adults normally return to the water in order to mate and to lay their eggs, but the young amphibian has gills and lives entirely in the water.

The frog's eggs are laid in the water. These develop into gilled tadpoles, which later grow limbs and climb onto the land.

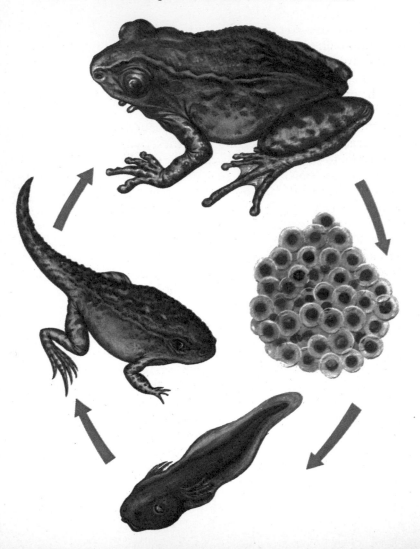

Gilled 'branchiosaur'
fossil larva

Although it is possible to study the life history of the living amphibians, we cannot always be so certain of that of the fossils. In some of them, however, a pattern of shallow grooves can be seen on the bones of the skull. Similar grooves in fish contain a 'lateral-line' sensory system that is used for detecting water-borne sounds. In some of the fossil amphibians these grooves are found only in smaller, and therefore younger specimens, indicating that these were aquatic.

It is rare to find the remains of really small fossils as their tiny bones are much more easily destroyed. Nevertheless, a number of tiny amphibians only two inches in length have been found, particularly in some Czechoslovakian coal deposits. Although these had external gills, it was at first thought that, like some living amphibians, they were a permanently aquatic type. It was only later that a series of stages were found, showing that these little branchiosaurs (as they were called) grew up, lost their gills and changed into terrestrial adults.

From these two clues, it seems likely, therefore, that the fossil amphibians had a life history like that of their living relatives, with an aquatic larval stage. The larvae of the amphibians cannot be said to have conquered the land. Furthermore, as we shall see, in most of the fossil amphibian groups as well, even the adult probably spent most or all of its time in the water. This is also true of many of the living amphibians, and even those adults that can live on land can do so only in fairly moist environments. It would perhaps be truer to say that the amphibians can tolerate the land, but they have never really conquered it.

The earliest known amphibian, 3 ft. long
Ichthyostega

First steps from the water

The largest and the best known of the early amphibians are the labyrinthodonts, so-called because their teeth had a labyrinthine structure like that of the rhipidistian fish (see page 31). These amphibians can be divided into two groups, the temnospondyls and the anthracosaurs, based on the pattern of the bones of their skulls.

The earliest labyrinthodont, *Ichthyostega,* was quite large and from Greenland, from the boundary between the Upper Devonian and the Mississippian. It is a tetrapod and not a fish, because it has normal tetrapod limbs and girdles. However, it still has a number of fish-like characteristics. These include a tail fin and a remnant of the bones that cover the gill chamber in a fish.

40

Like *Ichthyostega,* many of the later temnospondyls seem to be adapted for spending much of their time in the water. For example, none of the known Carboniferous (as the Mississippian and Pennsylvanian together are sometimes called) labyrinthodonts were wholly terrestrial. This may, however, be simply because most of them were found in coal-swamp deposits, whose fauna would naturally be aquatic, and terrestrial forms may have in fact existed, but not been preserved.

Even in the Permian, several types of temnospondyl seem to have lived wholly or largely in the water. This mode of life is indicated by the elaborate gill system and tiny limbs of such Permian forms as *Dvinosaurus* from Russia and *Archegosaurus* from Germany. The long snout of *Archegosaurus* suggests that it was probably a fish-eating amphibian. An even more elongate snout is found in the Triassic trematosaurs. These are found in marine deposits and, though little but their skulls are known, it seems, certain that they too were wholly aquatic fish-eaters.

Heads of some aquatic labyrinthodonts, *Archegosaurus* (*above*), *Dvinosaurus* (*below*) and the long-snouted trematosaur *Aphaneramma* (*right*)

Terrestrial amphibians

Though many of the temnospondyls stayed in the water, others probably spent a part of their time on land. *Eryops,* from the Lower Permian of the United States, was quite large and had a leathery skin with reduced scales. It looks as though it was quite capable of walking on land, though not very fast, but its rather large, flattened head suggests that it may have fed in water, perhaps on other amphibians or reptiles.

There are, in addition, a few groups which, though they may well have had aquatic larvae, probably spent nearly all of their adult life on land. Two such groups, which had slender limbs and seem to have been active terrestrial animals, are found in the same deposits as the remains of *Eryops.* An example of these groups is *Cacops,* which had a line of bony plates embedded down the middle of its back. Another labyrinthodont, *Peltobatrachus* from the Upper Permian of eastern Africa, had bony armor similar to an armadillo, with shields over the shoulder and hip regions and bands of armor in between.

5 ft. long *Eryops*

16 ins. long *Cacops*

28 ins. long
Peltobatrachus

42

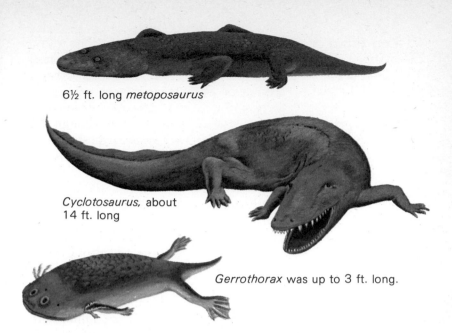

6½ ft. long *metoposaurus*

Cyclotosaurus, about
14 ft. long

Gerrothorax was up to 3 ft. long.

Back to the water

Although some of the temnospondyls 'experimented' with
land life during the Permian, nearly all of the Triassic forms,
known as stereospondyls, were aquatic. From early Triassic
times onward a gradual change occurred, ending in amphibians with long heavy snouts, poorly ossified bodies and
small limbs. Their builds and the presence of lateral-line
grooves on their skulls indicate that they were completely
aquatic forms, whose mode of life was probably very like
that of present-day crocodiles. Two independent lines can
be distinguished by the position of the eyes. These are far
back on the head in such forms as *Cyclotosaurus,* which
include the largest amphibian known, about 14 feet long, and
much farther forward in the other group, of which *Metoposaurus* is an example.

Though similarly aquatic, the Triassic plagiosaurs such as
Gerrothorax are quite different in appearance, for their skull
was short and wide, though very flattened. They were
probably like living angler-fish and lay on the bottom,
attracting animals into their open mouths by a fleshy-
colored lure.

Toward the reptiles

All the amphibians so far described belong to one of the two branches of the labyrinthodonts, the temnospondyls. The other branch, the anthracosaurs, includes only two groups. The first group, called the embolomeres, are nearly all found in Upper Carboniferous deposits. Their long tail with a dorsal fin, as shown in *Archeria,* indicates that they were aquatic, like the other amphibians of their period. From their long snout, it seems likely that they were fish-eaters.

The second group, mainly from the Lower Permian, are called the seymouriamorphs. As in most of the labyrinthodont groups, there are some aquatic forms, such as *Kotlassia,* but most of them were terrestrial. Some were quite small, such as the little scaled *Discosauriscus* from Germany, while others, such as *Seymouria* from the United States, were larger. The existence of several similarities between these terrestrial amphibians and the reptiles suggests that the reptiles may have evolved from the seymouriamorphs. Unfortunately these Permian forms, and even a few known Pennsylvanian seymouriamorphs, are too late in time to be actual ancestors of reptiles, which had already appeared early in the Carboniferous. Even earlier seymouriamorphs may well have existed but once again, since nearly all the Carboniferous faunas come from coal-swamp deposits, little is known of what was living and evolving in more terrestrial environments.

The main difference between living amphibians and reptiles lies in their life history. Amphibians lay their eggs in water (or in a very moist environment) and have aquatic larvae, while reptile eggs are laid on land, and are protected by a shell and the embryo develops within a series of membranes (see pages 50 to 51). The life history of the early tetrapods is uncertain. Some of them may, like the reptiles, have evolved a method of developing on land, but using a different method. They would then, strictly speaking, be neither amphibians nor reptiles. This might be true of any of the terrestrial temnospondyls, such as *Peltobatrachus* (see page 42). An example from the seymouriamorphs is *Diadectes* from the Lower Permian of the United States, which looks so completely adapted to terrestrial life that it was, until recently, regarded as a reptile.

A. 7 ft. long *Archeria*
B. 3 ft. long *Kotlassia*
C. 2 ft. long *Seymouria*
D. 10 ins. long *Discosauriscus*
E. 10 ft. long *Diadectes*

Toward the modern amphibians

The labyrinthodonts are mainly fairly large sized, but alongside them there lived a variety of scaly amphibians, known as lepospondyls. Most of these were only a few inches long and lived during the Upper Carboniferous. Many lived in the water and swam by lateral undulations of the body and tail. *Sauropleura,* for example, from Czechoslovakia, had a very powerful tail and reduced limbs. The limbs of *Diplocaulus,* from the Lower Permian of the United States, were also tiny, and its flattened head and body suggests that it spent most of its time on the bottom of lakes and ponds.

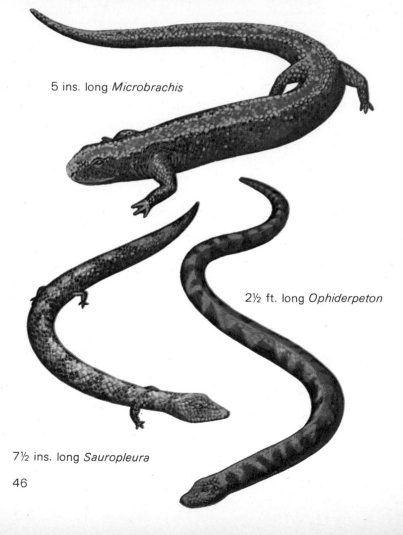

5 ins. long *Microbrachis*

2½ ft. long *Ophiderpeton*

7½ ins. long *Sauropleura*

Its head was broadened into an arrowhead shape, but the reason for this peculiarity is unknown. Other forms such as *Ophiderpeton,* which is found in both Europe and North America, had lost their limbs altogether and may have been burrowers.

Another group of leposondyls, called the microsaurs, also includes a number of semi-aquatic forms with an elongated body and reduced limbs, such as *Microbrachis* from Czechoslovakia. Other microsaurs, such as *Cardiocephalus* from the Lower Permian of the United States, are of particular interest as they were probably the ancestors of today's living amphibians. The lepospondyls, unlike the labyrinthodonts, have vertebrae that are very similar to those of the modern Amphibia. Nearly all the lepospondyls have limbs which are so reduced, or even lost, that it is very unlikely that they could ever have evolved into salamanders and frogs. Only *Cardiocephalus* and its relatives, therefore, remain as the possible source of the line which led to the three modern groups of amphibians: the salamanders, the frogs and toads, and the limbless, burrowing apodans.

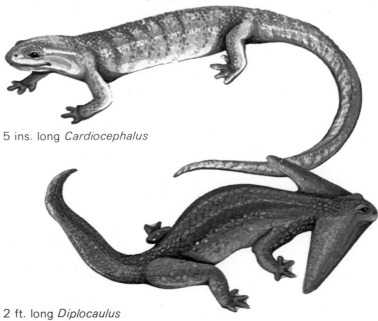

5 ins. long *Cardiocephalus*

2 ft. long *Diplocaulus*

Living amphibians

Although the jumping frogs and toads, the crawling newts and salamanders, and the burrowing apodans appear very different from one another, they all share one very peculiar feature. Unlike other vertebrates they absorb much of their oxygen through their skin. This may be because they do not use movement of the ribs to suck air in and out of the lungs, instead they pump it down, using the floor of the mouth as a bellows. This method only forces a mouthful of air to the lungs at each cycle of movement. This limited oxygen supply to the lungs is therefore supplemented by oxygen absorbed

South American horned frog toad

Tree-frog

through the skin. This has been made possible by loss of the scale covering and by the development of mucus glands that keep the skin moist. Because the skin has a tendency to dry up, the modern amphibians are therefore unable to live in very dry environments and must live in or near the water.

The fossil history of these amphibians is not well known, for they are mostly small and the skeleton of many is poorly ossified. The earliest recognizable frog comes from the Triassic of Madagascar. All the frogs and toads are very specialized for jumping, with long powerful hind legs. Although most of them live in the water or on the ground,

48

several types have sucking pads on their fingers and toes and live in trees.

The first member of the salamander and newt group is from the Jurassic. Many of these amphibians live in the water and some never leave it, such as *Megalobatrachus* from Japan, which may grow to five feet in length. Several, such as the congo eel (*Amphiuma*) of the United States, have reduced their limbs and burrow in the soft mud at the bottom of streams, feeding on invertebrates. The fossil history of the third group of living amphibians, the apodans, such as *Ichthyophis*, is quite unknown. They are completely limbless and burrow in moist earth, feeding on worms.

Two types of terrestrial salamander; some of these are lungless and only breathe by way of their skin.

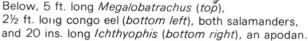

Below, 5 ft. long *Megalobatrachus* (*top*), 2½ ft. long congo eel (*bottom left*), both salamanders, and 20 ins. long *Ichthyophis* (*bottom right*), an apodan.

Conquest of the land

Few adult amphibians have mastered the difficulties of land life, and their larvae are normally aquatic. The real key to success on land was the development of the reptilian egg. Once this had appeared, the tetrapods no longer had to return to water to breed. The egg, found in both reptiles and birds, is deceptively simple in appearance. It is, however, responsible for protecting the developing embryo and its food supply from damage and desiccation, while still allowing it to obtain oxygen and to dispose of waste products. These functions are carred out by a series of embryonic membranes and the shell itself.

The amphibian larva starts to feed at an early stage. In reptiles, the presence of a large mass of yolk provides the food reserve needed for the much longer period of development it passes within the egg. This yolk is surrounded by a membrane in which a rich supply of blood vessels transports the food material to the embryo as it is required. The firm eggshell provides the necessary support for the yolk mass and for the developing embryo. Special pores in the shell allow oxygen to pass through, and this is picked up and transported to the embryo by blood vessels in another membrane, which is called the chorion, and which lies immediately under the shell. Another membrane, the amnion, encloses the embryo in a sac of liquid, ensuring that it does not become pressed against the shell or submerged in the yolk. The embryo also needs water, which is supplied by the albumen, or 'white' of the egg. Finally, the long stay within the egg means that the embryo will accumulate a fairly large quantity of waste products which would poison the embryo unless they were removed, and they are stored in yet another membrane, the allantois. This, and the enclosed waste products, are left behind when the young reptile hatches out.

These thin membranes and shell make it possible for the reptile embryo to carry on all the essential processes of life. It can then emerge from the protecting eggshell at an advanced stage of development, fairly well able to look after itself. This amniote egg gave the reptiles a decisive advantage over the amphibians and allowed them to dominate the world for over 150 million years.

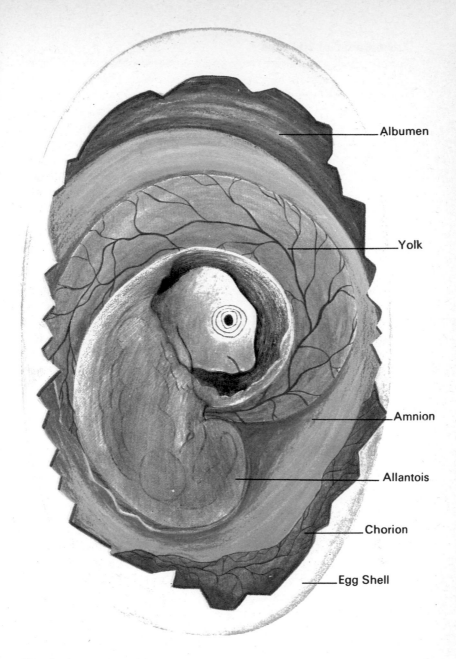

Albumen

Yolk

Amnion

Allantois

Chorion

Egg Shell

Developing turtle and its embryonic membranes inside the eggshell.

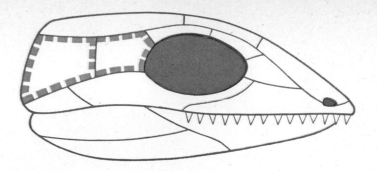

Anapsid type of skull as found in turtles and tortoises.

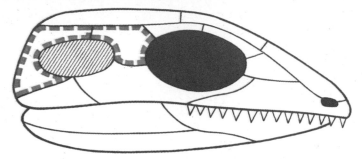

Synapsid type of skull found in the line that led to mammals.

An outline of reptilian evolution

The paleontologist has to rely heavily on the skeleton for his ideas on the relationship and evolution of vertebrates. It is therefore fortunate that the main lines of evolution of the reptiles are clearly seen in the structure of their skulls.

Like those of amphibians, the skulls of the earliest reptiles were solid and roof-like, pierced only by holes for the eyes and nostrils. This type, called an anapsid skull, is still to be seen in the living Chelonia—that is, the turtles and tortoises. It was also retained in two short-lived groups, the rather lizard-like procolophonids and the herbivorous pareiasaurs.

The other reptilian lineages developed further skull openings behind the eyes. These served to reduce the weight of the skull and permitted more room and power to the bulging muscles that closed the jaws. In one major line of reptiles, known as the synapsids, only one pair of these openings is found. These were the dominant reptiles of the

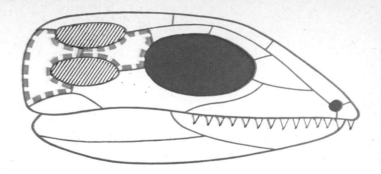

Diapsid type of skull found in many reptiles.

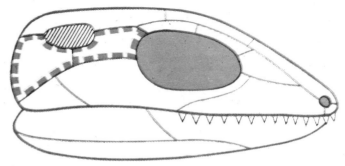

Euryapsid type of skull found in ichthyosaurs and plesiosaurs.

Permian and, although no synapsids are still alive today, it is from them that the mammals evolved.

In the other major line, known as the diapsids, two pairs of skull openings appeared. The diapsids replaced the synapsids as dominant reptiles during the Triassic and radiated into a great variety of dinosaurs and flying reptiles. Even today, the majority of living reptiles belong to this group, for crocodiles, lizards and snakes all have skulls based on this pattern. Furthermore, the birds are descendants of early diapsid reptiles.

These two main lines include nearly all the terrestrial reptiles, but two other groups returned to the sea and were extremely successful during the late Mesozoic. A final type of skull known as euryapsid, is found in the ichthyosaurs and plesiosaurs. The origins of these two aquatic groups are unknown but they were extremely successful during the late Mesozoic.

Tertiary	Turtles Snakes Lizards
Cretaceous	
Jurassic	To Mammals
Triassic	Procolophonids
Permian	Pareiasaurs saur
Pennsylvanian	

The first reptiles

Reptiles first appeared very early in the geological record. Ancestors of both main lines, the synapsids and diapsids, had appeared in the Mid-Carboniferous, so that their common ancestor must have evolved the amniote egg even earlier. These earliest reptiles are all quite small; only about a foot long, and they probably fed on insects and other invertebrate animals. *Hylonomus* from the Mid-Carboniferous of Canada and *Captorhinus* from the Lower Permian of the United States are both little anapsid reptiles of this kind, which are known as captorhinomorphs.

Hylonomus, 18 ins., one of the earliest known reptiles.

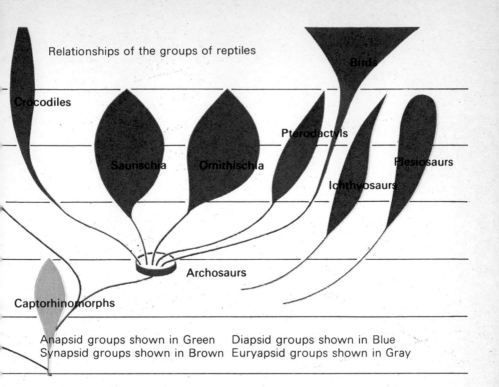

Relationships of the groups of reptiles

Crocodiles

Birds

Pterodactyls

Saurischia   Ornithischia

Plesiosaurs

Ichthyosaurs

Archosaurs

Captorhinomorphs

Anapsid groups shown in Green   Diapsid groups shown in Blue
Synapsid groups shown in Brown Euryapsid groups shown in Gray

Although we believe the diapsid radiation evolved from animals of this group, the captorhinomorphs became extinct at the end of the Permian. It is possible they died out because of competition from another group of insectivorous anapsids, called procolophonids. These appeared in the Permian and survived until nearly the end of the Triassic, and are known from deposits in South Africa, Europe and both North and South America. Some later genera, such as *Hypsognathus* from the United States, had bony spikes on the sides and back of the skull.

Hypsognathus, 1 ft. long, a Triassic procolophonid

The first land herbivores

The food cycle of living terrestrial vertebrates is based on the land plants, for the terrestrial carnivores feed on terrestrial herbivores. The pattern of life was, however, different when the first reptiles appeared.

There were plenty of little invertebrates for such reptiles as the captorhinomorphs and procolophonids to feed on, but there were no larger terrestrial animals to provide food for a terrestrial carnivore. Although, by evolving the amniote egg, the reptiles had at last made their life history independent of the water, they still ultimately depended on it as a source of food. The earliest carnivorous reptiles were semi-aquatic, rather like crocodiles in their habits. They fed on amphibians which were themselves fish-eaters. An anapsid reptile of this kind is *Limnoscelis,* which came from the Lower Permian of the United States. As is later shown (on pages 58 to 59) the earliest synapsid reptiles were very similar in their habits and in their diet.

It was not until the time of the Middle Permian that the first common herbivorous reptiles appeared. These animals,

Limnoscelis, a semi-aquatic early reptile, about 5 ft. long

Bradysaurus, a pareiasaur about 8 ft. long, one of the first plant-eating reptiles.

which were called the pareiasaurs, have been discovered in South Africa, Russia and Scotland. Like the captorhinomorphs, procolophonids and *Limnoscelis* that have already been discussed, they were anapsids.

The body of a herbivore must be very bulky, for plant material is extremely difficult to digest and has to remain in the body for a long time. In the pareiasaurs this bulky body is still supported in the primitive fashion, by slinging it between the limbs, and their appearance is therefore very ungainly. This was accentuated by the development of bony projections on the skull. In some, at least, parts of the back were also covered by small bony plates that were embedded in the flesh.

The pareiasaurs were quite large animals, reaching a size of up to 8 feet long and 5 feet high. They appear to have lived in rather swampy conditions where the plant growth would have been particularly abundant. They did not flourish for long, for they became extinct well before the end of the Permian.

Reptiles with sails

The most primitive synapsid or mammal-like reptiles are called the pelycosaurs. They include three different groups that appeared in the Pennsylvanian and survived until the Middle Permian. They were all semi-squatic animals, with the ungainly posture of a primitive tetrapod. A peculiar feature found in some examples of all three groups is the development of a sail-like membrane stretched between the elongated vertebrae of the back. This membrane was prob-

Dimetrodon, a sail-bearing carnivorous pelycasaur, 11 ft. long

ably a primitive method of regulating the temperature of the body. If it was feeling cold, the reptile would turn broadside to the sun's rays and the membrane would absorb heat. Similarly, if the reptile were too warm it would face the sun, so that the rays would pass parallel to the sail and absorb very little heat.

Two of these pelycosaur groups were carnivorous and must have eaten the labyrinthodont amphibians which are found in the same deposits. *Ophiacodon* and *Dimetrodon* are examples of these two groups. *Dimetrodon* was up to 11 feet long and must have been the dominant carnivore of its time.

Ophiacodon, 7 ft. long,
a meat-eating pelycosaur.

We believe that the more advanced mammal-like reptiles evolved from that group to which *Dimetrodon* belongs, for they are alike in several ways.

Edaphosaurus is a member of the third pelycosaur group. Its skull is very powerfully built, with batteries of crushing teeth, and these pelycosaurs probably fed on the shellfish of the low-lying swampy areas where they seem to have lived.

Another group, called the caseids, seems to have been the very first group of terrestrial herbivorous reptiles. These bulky pelycosaurs, such as *Cotylorhynchus* which weighed about 700 pounds, were not very successful, and are found only rarely in the Lower Permian.

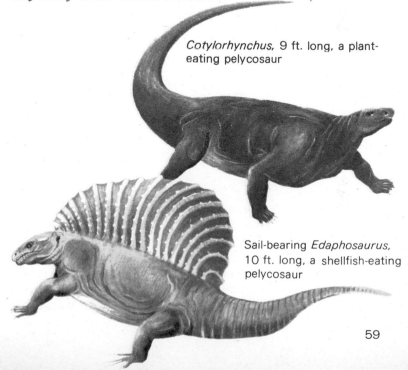

Cotylorhynchus, 9 ft. long, a plant-eating pelycosaur

Sail-bearing *Edaphosaurus,* 10 ft. long, a shellfish-eating pelycosaur

Two primitive therapsids:
Titanosuchus (*left*) and
Moschops (*right*) were both
about 8 ft. long.

Herds of reptiles

By the middle of the Permian the pelycosaurs were extinct.
They were succeeded by a variety of more advanced synapsids, which are known collectively as the therapsids. These
reptiles are best known from the rich fossil-bearing deposits
of the South African Karroo Beds, in which erosion reveals
hundreds of new specimens every year.

In the earliest of these beds lived two closely related
groups of synapsids, one carnivorous and one herbivorous.
The sharp teeth of the titanosuchids indicate that they must
have preyed upon the tapinocephalids such as *Moschops,*
whose peg-like teeth are adapted to browsing on soft vegetation. Both groups are rather clumsy in appearance and were
soon replaced by two more advanced groups of synapsids,
the dicynodonts and the gorgonopsids.

The dicynodonts are so named because they usually have
a pair of tusk-like canine teeth. Though other teeth, too, are
present in some little dicynodonts, which may have been
insectivorous, in most forms these have been replaced by a
horny, turtle-like beak. These animals ranged in size considerably from that of a rabbit to that of a rhinoceros, and a
great variety of the dicynodonts were probably abundant
throughout the Upper Permian in all parts of the world,

except in Australia. A hippopotamus-like semi-aquatic genus, *Lystrosaurus,* is found in the Lower Triassic, and a few large genera such as *Dinodontosaurus* survived until the Upper Triassic, co-existing with the early dinosaurs.

The herds of the Permian dicynodonts provided a food supply for the more active carnivorous gorgonopsids. Of slender build and with long stabbing canine teeth, gorgonopsids such as *Lycaenops* quite probably must have preyed upon the dicynodonts as, about 250 million years later, the saber-tooth cats hunted the herds of thick-skinned herbivorous mammals.

Advanced therapsids:
Lycaenops (*top*) 3½ ft. long.
Lystrosaurus (*middle*) 3 to 4 ft.
long. *Dinodontosaurus* (*bottom*),
6 ft. long

Progressive mammal-like reptiles

Although successful in their day, neither the gorgonopsids nor the dicynodonts really merit the term mammal-like, for they probably had not yet evolved the activity and the hair-covering that are associated with the mammals. However, alongside them in South Africa lived the earliest members of two lines of synapsids which were to evolve into animals that may have been very mammal-like in their habits and appearance. Both these lines, for example, developed a bony false palate, separating the mouth from the passage through which the air is inhaled into the lungs—a structure which is found also in the mammals.

Both these progressive groups, which are called the bauriamorphs and the cynodonts, were fairly small omnivores or carnivores. One significant difference between them, however, can be observed in their cheek teeth. The bauriamorphs, such as *Bauria,* had simple pointed cheek teeth similar to those of the reptiles today. In the cynodonts such as *Thrinaxodon,* on the other hand, the crowns of these teeth bear a complicated pattern of little cusps and ridges, like those of the mammals.

The bauriamorphs are unknown after the Lower Triassic,

3 ft. long *Bauria* (*above*) and 1½ ft. long *Thrinaxodon* (*below*)

6 ft. long *Cynognathus*

3 ft. long *Bienotherium*

20 ins. long *Oligokyphus*

but the cynodonts and their descendants survived for a much longer period. Some of the Triassic cynodonts, such as *Cynognathus,* were about the size of a pig and may have used the complex crowns of their cheek teeth for grinding up hard vegetable matter. Such types include various Middle Triassic cynodonts found in both Africa and South America, and also *Bienotherium,* a tritylodont from the Upper Triassic of China. The tritylodonts, such as *Oligokyphus,* were the last group of mammal-like reptiles, surviving into the Jurassic, and are probably descendants of the cynodonts.

63

The new reptiles

The synapsids dominated the world for about 65 million years, through the whole of the Permian and much of the Triassic, and their descendants were to dominate it throughout the Tertiary. But, for the 130 million years of the Jurassic and Cretaceous, this line of evolution was eclipsed by the rise of the diapsid reptiles. The change began in the Lower and Middle Triassic, when primitive ancestors of the dinosaurs appear and the radiation of the synapsids tapers off. We cannot be sure why the synapsids were unable to compete successfully with these diapsids. Many of the diapsids tended to be bipedal (i.e. to run on their hind legs alone), and this may have given them a decisive speed advantage over the synapsids in catching prey or in escaping predators. Even if this were so, it might itself merely be a result of some difference in the physiological capabilities of the two groups. For example, the dinosaurs might have developed a more efficient method of changing the air in the lungs, or of controlling their body temperature. Such characteristics leave no trace in a fossil, and we may therefore never know what advantages allowed the dinosaurs to begin their long reign.

Though the dinosaurs were the most successful of all the diapsids, several other lines are known. The pterosaurs crocodiles and birds are all descended from the same branch as are the dinosaurs—a branch known as the archosaurs. The other diapsid branch, known as lepidosaurs, includes the living lizards and snakes, and a number of rather bizarre Triassic groups.

Anapsid skull
of a turtle

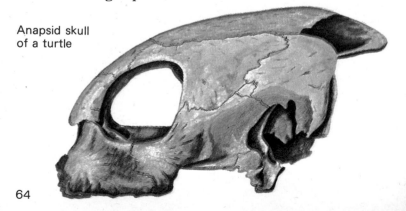

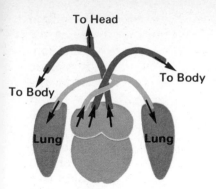

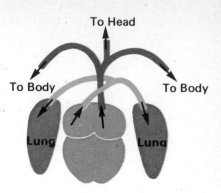

In chelonians and diapsids the main vessel which supplies blood to the head and body has split into right and left portions.

In mammals, and presumably in their ancestors the synapsids, this split has not taken place.

Although their skulls are anapsid, the anatomy of the ankle, the heart and the blood system of tortoises and turtles shows many similarities to these systems in living diapsids. These structures are quite different in mammals, which are descended from the synapsid reptiles. It seems likely, therefore, that the tortoise and turtle group, known as the Chelonia, belongs to the diapsid line of reptilian evolution but diverged before this line had developed the characteristic openings in the skull.

In chelonians and diapsids the fifth metatarsal bone is L-shaped.

In synapsids and mammals the fifth metatarsal bone is straight.

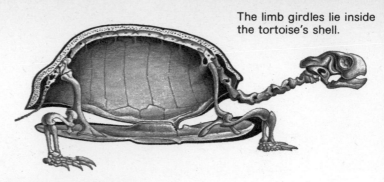

The limb girdles lie inside the tortoise's shell.

Tortoises and turtles

Nothing is known of the earliest history of the Chelonia. The first member of the group, *Proganochelys* from the Middle Triassic of Germany, is already a fully developed chelonian, giving no hint of its own ancestry. The tortoises and turtles are heavily armored and are also specialized in having lost their teeth, which have been replaced by a horny beak.

The massive bony shell, covered with horny plates, is fused on to the trunk vertebrae and the ribs. The limbs, head and tail can usually be withdrawn inside this protective shell. This has led to a great change in the position of the shoulder girdle, which in normal vertebrates is placed outside the rib cage. In the Chelonia, the shell and the ribs to which it is fused have grown outward to enclose the shoulder girdle and its limb muscles. To give maximum stability the tortoise's feet are placed well out to the side, and the upper parts of the limbs therefore project sideways. To give maximum clearance, the underside of the shell is flat and the body is short, including only ten trunk vertebrae. The neck is usually bent upward into an S when the head is withdrawn. There exists, however, a group in which the neck is withdrawn sideways. In the box-turtles, hinged portions of the shell enclose the limbs and head when they have been retracted inside the shell.

Nearly all the living families of chelonians appeared in the Jurassic or Cretaceous. Most of them, like the pond-turtles and sea-turtles, have taken up an amphibian or aquatic existence, so that the weight of their armor is supported by

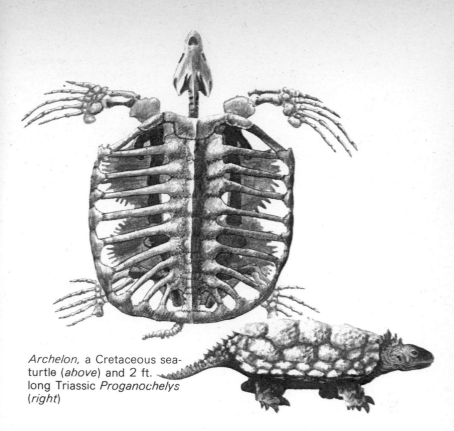

Archelon, a Cretaceous sea-turtle (*above*) and 2 ft. long Triassic *Proganochelys* (*right*)

the water—the largest known chelonian is the Cretaceous sea-turtle *Archelon,* 12 feet long. Some of these aquatic turtles are strong swimmers, using powerful paddle-like feet, and have reduced their bony armor. Land tortoises such as *Testudo* and others, are members of the only group of fully terrestrial herbivorous chelonians. A few species of *Testudo* living on isolated islands where there are no predators have become giants up to 4 feet long and weighing 560 pounds.

Land-tortoise (*right*) and Sea-turtle (*below*)

67

Lizards and their relatives — the lepidosaurs

Only one living lizard relative still has the primitive diapsid type of skull. Called *Sphenodon,* and last of a line known as far back as the Triassic, it is found only on a few small islands off the coast of New Zealand. It is unusual in having a third light sensitive eye-like structure, called a pineal eye, on top of its head. This lies below a special small hole in the skull, which is found in many fossil fish, amphibians and reptiles. The functions of this rudimentary third eye are still uncertain, but it seems to be concerned with sensing the temperature around the animal, rather than with vision.

18 ins. long lizard-like
Tuatara, *Sphenodon*

The only living rhynchocephalian

Some pig-sized Triassic relatives of *Sphenodon,* which are known as rhynchosaurs, are the only successful herbivorous group that evolved from the lepidosaurs. The toothless front ends of their jaws were pointed and resemble a pair of pincers, while the back teeth were fused into a set of wide tooth plates. The rhynchosaurs have been discovered all over the world, except Australia, in the Middle and Upper Triassic.

3 ft. long
rhynchosaur

Many of the living families of lizards are known first in Upper Jurassic rocks. Most of them are little active omnivores or carnivores, usually including invertebrate animals in their diet. *Iguana* is a typical American lizard, while the Australian *Moloch* is, like many desert-living lizards, covered with spines. Another lizard, *Amblyrhynchus,* feeds on seaweed off the Galapagos Islands in the Pacific. Several types are specially adapted for climbing. The geckos can climb up panes of glass, using ridged pads on their feet, and the chameleons use their grasping feet and prehensile tail to cling to branches. They are also notable for their ability to change color, and for their long sticky-tipped tongue, which can be shot out to capture an insect nearly a foot away.

Old World chameleon

Gecko with 'adhesive' toes

Motoch, an Australian lizard

Tylosaurus, a mosasaur, or marine lizard

Strange lizards

Perhaps the most incredible fossil vertebrate that has ever been discovered is a creature called *Tanystropheus*, which is probably related to the lizards. Its total length was about 13 feet, but over 6 feet of this was taken up by an exceedingly long neck, and over 4 feet by its tail, with the result that its body was only 2 feet long. The long neck was not very flexible, for it was composed of only ten vertebrae. It was not held upward like that of a giraffe, but horizontally. *Tanystropheus* lived near the shores of the Muschelkalk Sea, which covered much of Central Europe during the Middle Triassic. It has been suggested that its long neck might have allowed it to scavenge out into the shallow margins of this sea, but the exact mode of life of this grotesque reptile is still quite unknown.

The Upper Triassic rocks of Great Britain and the eastern United States have yielded a few specimens of little gliding lizards such as *Kuehneosaurus*. The ribs of these little fossils are greatly elongated and must have supported a gliding membrane much like that of *Draco*, a living lizard which, after launching itself from the branches of a tree, can glide for 20 to 30 feet.

Kuehneosaurus, a flying lizard, was 2½ ft. long.

The only thoroughly aquatic lizards that have been discovered were the mosasaurs, which lived in the seas during the Upper Cretaceous. They were about 20 feet in length and they swam by beating their powerful tail from side to side. They include a variety of types, most of which were probably fish-eaters, such as *Tylosaurius,* although one called *Globidens* had hemispherical crushing teeth and probably fed on mollusks.

Tanystropheus, a Triassic lizard relative, was up to 13 ft. long.

71

Life without limbs

Lizards, like nearly all reptiles, undulate from side to side as they move. For a lizard living in thick grass, or in a sandy area or burrow, this undulation is quite sufficient to move the animal forward. The sides of the body push backward against any projecting pieces of vegetation or soil, while the scales and the ends of the ribs push against the ground under the body. The limbs are of little help, and, in many such lizards, have been lost.

Stages in the loss of the limbs can still be seen in members of a group of lizards known as the skinks—in the genus *Chalcides* of northern Africa, for example, the limbs are extremely tiny. Lizards that have lost the limbs altogether include the European slow-worm and the tropical amphisbaenids. Another example is *Ophisaurus* of Asia and America, often called the glass-snake because it can break off its tail if attacked. This method of distracting the attention of the predator is common in lizards but lacking in all true snakes.

Snakes are merely the descendants of another group of lizards that, sometime in the Mesozoic, similarly became limbless. This particular group has become very successful. Lacking limbs or cutting-teeth, snakes must swallow their prey whole, and special modifications of the skeleton

Some lizards with reduced limbs

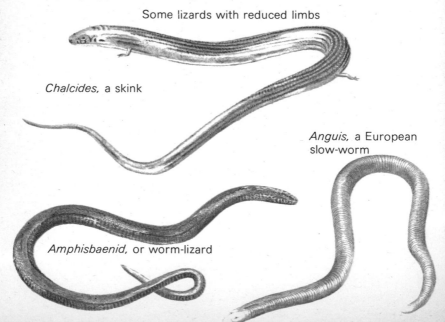

Chalcides, a skink

Anguis, a European
slow-worm

Amphisbaenid, or worm-lizard

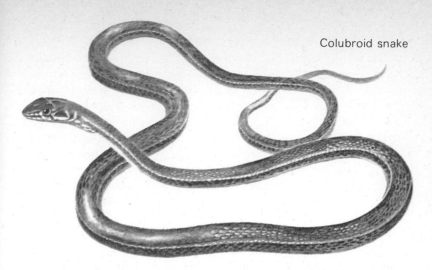

Colubroid snake

make it possible for them to swallow animals much larger than themselves.

Apart from a few little burrowing forms, the most primitive snakes are the pythons and boas, known since the Upper Cretaceous. Up to about 30 feet long, these snakes can suffocate their prey by encircling them and squeezing, so that they cannot breathe. All other snakes belong to a group known as the colubroids, which appeared in the early Tertiary. These snakes are far smaller and the size of prey they can catch and kill, using their fang-like teeth alone, is also usually small. The development of fast-acting poisons injected through the fangs has allowed some of them, such as rattlesnakes, to kill larger animals.

Boa

Early archosaurs

Triassic rocks contain remains of the earliest members of the archosaurs, the line of diapsid evolution that was to culminate in the dinosaurs and pterosaurs, and which is represented today by the crocodiles. One of the first archosaurs, *Shansisuchus,* is found in the early Triassic deposits of China. About 13 feet long, with a powerful head and dentition, it must have preyed upon the herbivorous dicynodonts and cynodonts of its day. *Chasmatosaurus* is another carnivorous archosaur found in these rocks. About 4 feet long, it became very crocodile-like in its habits but had a peculiar downturned snout.

Triassic archosaurs

Shansisuchus,
13 ft. long

Chasmatorsaurus, 4 ft. long

Rutiodon is a member of the phytosaurs, a common group in Upper Triassic rocks of North America and Eurasia. Their nostrils lie far back, between the eyes, not at the end of the elongate snout as in crocodiles. As a result, they did not need to develop the false palate, separating the air passage from the mouth, such as is found in crocodiles (see page 76).

The body of the phytosaurs was covered with bony plates.

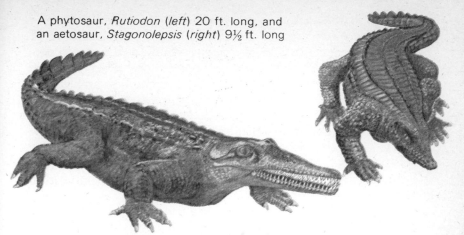
A phytosaur, *Rutiodon* (*left*) 20 ft. long, and an aetosaur, *Stagonolepis* (*right*) 9½ ft. long

A similar armor is found in the Upper Triassic aetosaurs such as *Stagonolepis,* which seems to have been herbivorous, for it has a small head with a blunt, rooting snout.

The bipedal tendency was to become very important in the archosaurs. Like some modern lizards, many archosaurs could use their long heavy tail to balance their body and could run on their hind limbs alone. In some cases this posture became permanent, and the hands could then become adapted for grasping or for flying. The tendency to bipedalism appears very early in the history of the archosaurs. One of the earliest members of the group is the little (3 feet long) reptile *Euparkeria* from the Lower Triassic of South Africa. Its hind limbs are noticeably larger than its forelimbs, and *Euparkeria* had clearly developed the ability to run on its hind limbs when it wished to move quickly.

Euparkeria, a two-legged ardiosaur ancestral to dinosaurs.

The first crocodile,
Protosuchus, 2½ ft. long

Living archosaurs — the crocodiles

Like several other groups of early archosaurs, the crocodiles
are a line that became semi-aquatic, feeding on fish and on
other reptiles and mammals when they came to the water to
drink. The nostrils lie at the front end of a very elongate
snout, and a long bony false palate has developed which,
together with fleshy flaps at the back of the mouth, ensures
that water does not enter the windpipe. In other ways the
skull is very primitive, for crocodiles are the only reptiles,
apart from the lepidosaurian *Sphenodon* (see page 68), that
still show the diapsid pattern of skull openings. They have
also retained the horn-covered bony plates, sunk in the skin,
that are found in most archosaurs.

A primitive form of crocodile called *Protosuchus* is found
in Upper Triassic rocks in the United States, and others are
known from slightly earlier rocks. A considerable variety of
crocodiles had evolved by Jurassic and Cretaceous times,

Geosaurus, 15 ft. long, a
marine crocodile

including a short-lived marine group. These lived during the Upper Jurassic and Lower Cretaceous when forms such as *Geosaurus,* which had developed paddle-shaped limbs and a fish-like tail, are found. South American genera, such as *Baurusuchus* of the Cretaceous, are another unusual line, which had only a short false palate and a small number of unusually large teeth.

Crocodiles of modern type first appeared in the Lower Cretaceous. They include the largest crocodile known, *Deinosuchus* of the Upper Cretaceous. This was 40 to 50 feet long and must have preyed on the great dinosaurs when they came to drink. Living forms include *Crocodilus* itself, the very similar but wider-snouted alligator, and the narrow-snouted fish-eating gavials.

Deinosuchus, a giant crocodile, 50 ft. long

A modern gavial, 15 ft. long

The dinosaurs

Some time in the Triassic, a group of archosaurs must have evolved a new adaptive feature, concerned perhaps with their methods of breathing, or of circulating their blood, or of regulating their body temperature.

Although we cannot be certain of this, it is the most likely explanation of the fact that the synapsids, which had provided most of the land vertebrates for over 60 million years, were relatively quickly replaced by archosaurs. Both in numbers and in variety, these archosaurs consisted mainly of the great reptiles popularly called dinosaurs.

Although it is convenient to call them all dinosaurs, this word includes two different groups of large Mesozoic reptiles. They can be distinguished by the structure of their pelvic girdles. In one group, the Saurischia, the pubis is directed downward and forward. In the other group, the Ornithischia, it runs downward and backward, and also extends further upward and forward.

Like such Lower Triassic forms as *Euparkeria* (see page 75), from which they probably evolved, most of the Saurischia were probably bipedal carnivores. One saurischian line which had become herbivorous was quadrupedal, however, for it is difficult to support the bulky body of a herbivore upon only two legs.

In contrast with the Saurischia, all the Ornithischia were herbivorous animals and many were quadrupedal. At the front end of the jaws, they had developed a special toothless section that must have been used to crop vegetation.

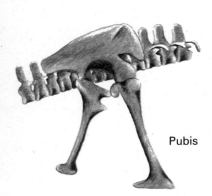

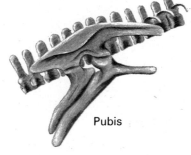

Pubis

Pubis

The saurischian type of pelvis (*left*) and the ornithischian type (*right*)

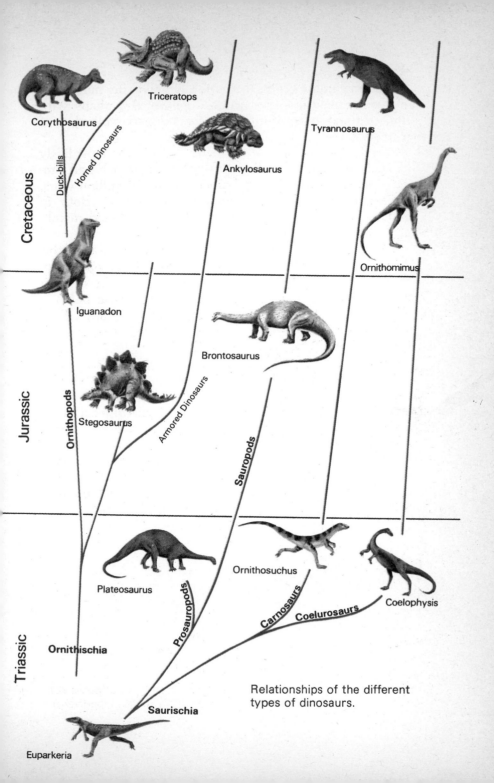

Corythosaurus

Triceratops

Ankylosaurus

Tyrannosaurus

Duck-bills

Horned Dinosaurs

Cretaceous

Iguanadon

Ornithomimus

Brontosaurus

Ornithopods

Stegosaurus

Armored Dinosaurs

Jurassic

Sauropods

Plateosaurus

Ornithosuchus

Coelophysis

Prosauropods

Carnosaurs

Coelurosaurs

Triassic

Ornithischia

Saurischia

Relationships of the different types of dinosaurs.

Euparkeria

Piece of mummified skin from a duck-billed dinosaur.

Horned dinosaur nest from Mongolia.

The size of dinosaurs

Only the hard bony parts of the vertebrates remain as fossils, but they are only a small part of an animal's body. No less important were its soft tissues and body chemistry, although even these aspects can be recreated with some confidence if it were a member of a group that is still alive today. There is no reason, for example, to think that fossil crocodiles had hearts, lungs or life histories very different from those of their living descendants.

The dinosaurs' conquest of the synapsid-dominated early Triassic world implies that they had evolved some new structure or process that gave them a vital advantage which allowed them to remain the dominant land animals for over 100 million years. Then, as decisively as their dominance began, it ended, and no really close relative of the dinosaurs survives. Furthermore, the size of these largest of land vertebrates involves problems faced by no living creature.

For these reasons, paleontologists would like to know more about dinosaurs. For example, why did they grow so large? A large animal certainly has many advantages over a smaller one. It can cover greater distances, go longer

80

without food or water, be more successful in contests for a mate and be less vulnerable. All these advantages, however, would be gained by any large animal. Why, then, did the dinosaurs alone reach such a gigantic size?

The climates of the Mesozoic were generally warm and mild over much of the earth, and plant growth may have been unusually luxuriant. These factors may first have allowed the dinosaurs to become larger. But as they grew in size, they would have found that they were gaining a new ability to control their body temperature. This is very important, for many of the body's functions depend on chemical reactions, the speed of which vary with the temperature. For this reason, the activity of an animal that cannot control its body temperature will vary too.

The ability of a bird or mammal to keep its body temperature constant depends mainly on its body covering. The dinosaurs had no warm covering to their body, for their skin was covered with little bony scales. But a large dinosaur's size helped it to control its temperature. An animal loses or gains heat through its body surface. As it becomes larger, its surface area increases far more slowly than its volume— the surface area of a 2 inch cube (24 square inches) is three times its volume (8 cubic inches), while that of a 6 inch cube (216 square inches) is the same as its volume (216 cubic inches). The rate of heat loss or gain through the skin of a large dinosaur would therefore be very small compared with the great amount of heat that was contained in its vast body, and over the course of a day its body temperature would change very slowly.

If these theories are correct, the body temperature of a younger, smaller dinosaur must have been more variable. We know that dinosaurs laid eggs, for their nests, containing up to thirty eggs, have been found in Mongolia. The hatching dinosaur cannot, therefore, have been too large, for mechanical and developmental problems seem to limit the maximum size of an egg to about a foot across. The young dinosaurs probably regulated their temperature in the same way as modern reptiles, by keeping in the sun or in the shade. They probably grew very rapidly so as to shorten the period before their size alone made them thermally independent.

Giant herbivores

Among the first dinosaurs discovered were the prosauropods, found in Upper Triassic deposits. As they had already diverged into carnivorous and herbivorous types, their common ancestor must have existed even earlier than this time. The carnivorous prosauropods are still extremely poorly known, but complete skeletons of such herbivorous types as *Plateosaurus*, which was 21 feet in length, have been found in South Africa and Europe. They had not progressed very far toward a bipedal posture, because the forelimbs of these animals were still quite large.

Diplodocus, a giant sauropod, 9 ft. long

The prosauropods did not survive into the Jurassic, for they were replaced by more progressive dinosaurs. The new herbivores, which probably evolved from early prosauropods, were called the sauropods. These great dinosaurs such as *Diplodocus* of the Upper Jurassic, were up to 90 feet in length, although much of this was taken up by a very long neck and tail.

The body of these animals is very bulky and *Brontosaurus*, which was a somewhat shorter but stockier relative of *Diplodocus*, may have weighed about 30 tons. This great weight was supported by four pillar-like limbs that ended in broad feet similar to those of an elephant. Even with these adaptations, moving this tonnage on land must have taken a great deal of energy. This, and the fact that the eyes and nostrils are often very high up on the skull, like those of a hippopotamus, suggests that these dinosaurs may have been amphibious.

Much of the life of these huge beasts may have been spent in lakes, where their weight would be supported by the

Brachiosaurus, a
50 ton sauropod

Plateosaurus, 2 ft. long,
a Triassic forerunner of
the sauropods

water. It is even possible that their body contained air sacs and floated near to the surface while their long neck allowed the head to browse on the plant growth that was on the bottom of the lake.

The largest sauropod of all was *Brachiosaurus* from the Upper Jurassic of Eastern Africa and North America. Eighty feet long, it was unusual in having front legs longer than the hind legs. These, and its long neck, would have given this 50 ton dinosaur a height of about 40 feet, if it raised its neck nearly vertically, considerably higher than a three-story building!

Two early carnivorous
dinosaurs, 8 ft. long
Coelophysis (*left*) and
12 ft. long *Ornithosuchus*
(*below*)

Great carnivores

The two main lines of carnivorous saurischians are called the
coelurosaurs and the carnosaurs. Both lines, which were
fully bipedal, began in the Upper Triassic. The slender
coelurosaurs were the more primitive of these groups. Some
were as small as a chicken and none were very large. A
typical early member was *Coelophysis* from the Upper Triassic of the United States. This little dinosaur was about 8
feet long, with a very long slender neck and tail. The forelimbs were fairly small, with only three fingers. These would
have been used in feeding or in slow walking, but *Coelophysis* would certainly have run on its hind limbs alone.

Very similar to the coelurosaurs are toothless and beaked
Cretaceous forms such as *Ornithomimus*. Although its
forelimbs are slightly longer than those of *Coelophysis*, its
hind limbs are far more powerful. It seems quite possible

Tyrannosaurus, 47 ft. long and 19 ft. high, a giant carnivorous dinosaur

that this swift ostrich-like dinosaur lived on the eggs of its larger relatives.

The existence of the great herbivorous sauropods made it possible for the forces of natural selection to produce giant carnivores that preyed upon them. These carnosaurs had short, heavy necks and large heads with powerful jaws. The earliest member, *Ornithosuchus* of the Upper Triassic of Scotland, was about 12 feet long. Jurassic carnosaurs such as *Allosaurus* of North America were over 30 feet long, and the evolution of the group culminated in *Tyrannosaurus* and its relatives of the late Cretaceous. Up to 47 feet long and 19 feet high when standing upright, they are the largest terrestrial carnivores ever known. The tiny front limbs at best served as props for rising after resting, and *Tyrannosaurus* must have torn flesh from its prey with its 6 inch long teeth.

Boneheads and duck-bills

Unlike the Saurischia, all the Ornithischia were herbivorous
—the front part of the jaws was toothless and horn-covered
in all of them. Many ornithischians were quadrupedal, but a
variety of forms known as ornithopods had fairly small front
limbs and were doubtless bipedal when running quickly.

The best known of all the ornithopods is *Iguanodon* from
Europe. In the Lower Cretaceous a herd of more than twenty
of these dinosaurs was buried. The rocks that covered their
remains were coal-bearing, and the skeletons were discovered
in 1877 when this coal was being mined. The adults were
about 30 feet long. Their front limbs were moderate in size,
with little hoof-like nails, and the thumb formed a large, pointed bony spike, which must have been an effective weapon of
defense. Although there was only a single row of teeth in
each jaw of earlier ornithopods, *Iguanodon* had a battery of
several rows of teeth, so that new teeth were continually
erupting as the older ones, worn out, dropped from the jaws.
Late Jurassic Camptosaurus of North America was a close
relative of *Iguanodon* but did not have a spiked thumb.

Two ornithopods: *Iguanodon* (*left*) and
a hadrosaur, or duck-bill (*below*)

86

2 ft. long head of *Pachycephalosaurus,*
a Cretaceous bone head

A later ornithopod, Pachucephalosaurus, had the roof of its
skull formed of a solid mass of bone over 10 inches thick.

The late Cretaceous hadrosaurs were about 30 feet long,
and the nasal passages in these ornithopods had developed
into a variety of crests, domes or horns that project from the
top of the skull. No convincing explanation of the function
of these structures has been found. The hadrosaurs are often
called duck-billed dinosaurs, for the toothless front part of
their jaws is very large. Behind this lies an even more elaborate battery of teeth than that of *Iguanodon*—one form
had about a thousand teeth in its jaws. The hands and feet
were webbed, which suggests that the hadrosaurs could
swim when necessary, probably by lashing their powerful
tails from side to side.

Some of the types of hadrosaur nasal crests

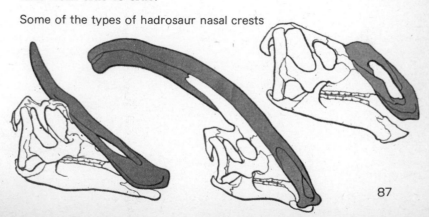

87

Plated and armored dinosaurs,
20 ft. long *Stegosaurus* (*left*)
and 15 ft. long *Ankylosaurus* (*below*)

Armored dinosaurs

The bipedal ornithopods could probably evade their enemies
by their speed. The slower quadrupedal ornithischians
managed to survive by developing a variety of types of
armor and horns, and may have aided each other by moving
in herds.

One of the best known is *Stegosaurus* of the late Jurassic
of North America. About 20 feet long, the bulky body of this
herbivore is carried clear of the ground by a great development of the hind limbs, twice the length of the forelimbs.
The back is protected by two rows of bony plates, the bases
of which were sunk into the flesh. Two pairs of bony spikes
near the end of the tail must have been used as defensive
weapons. Stegosaurs are called plated dinosaurs.

The stegosaurs were succeeded in the Cretaceous by a
differently armored group, the ankylosaurs. These ornithischians, such as the 15-foot long *Ankylosaurus* of North
America, had a flattened body. This was covered by an
almost continuous mosaic of bony plates that also protected
the head. Long protective spines extended outward from the
edges of this armor. The tail was armored in various ways
in the ankylosaurs, with rings of bone, with bony spikes, or
with a large club-like mass of bone. Both the stegosaurs and
the ankylosaurs must have fed on soft vegetation, for the

Triceratops, 20 ft. long, a horned dinosaur

teeth are very small and weak or, in some cases, lacking.

The last ornithischians were the Upper Cretaceous ceratopsians of North America and Asia. Up to 20 feet long, they had a narrow parrot-like beak, behind which was a battery of teeth very like that of the hadrosaurs. Although their body was unarmored, their neck was protected by a great frill of bone that projected from the back of the skull. This frill seems to have developed originally as an attachment for the muscles running down onto the jaws. Their main defense was the presence of sharp bony horns that projected from the front of the head in rhinoceros-like fashion. *Triceratops* had three of these horns, *Monoclonius* only one, while the little (7 feet long) *Protoceratops* had only a small bump on its nose.

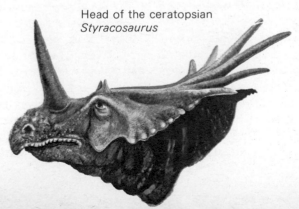

Head of the ceratopsian
Styracosaurus

Flying reptiles

Because the archosaurs were bipedal, their forelimbs were not used in walking and could be modified. In the pterosaurs and the birds, they became adapted for flight. The pterosaur wing was a leathery membrane like that of a bat. It was supported by very elongate bones of the wrist and fourth finger. In primitive Jurassic pterosaurs, the tail is long and ended in a leathery membrane that must have functioned as a rudder. The absence of a bird-like keel on the breastbone means the pterosaurs cannot have had strong flight muscles. They must have relied on gliding, like an albatross.

The next problem is how they got into the air. Neither the wing muscles nor the weak hind limbs of a pterosaur would have been capable of lifting them from the ground, and they must have lived on cliffs, where upcurrents of wind would help them to rise. Their wings, however, could not be folded away very neatly, so that they must have been too clumsy and vulnerable to predators to live on the ground at the cliff top. The presence of small clawed vestiges of the first three fingers suggests that they may have hung, bat-like, from ledges on the cliffs. Even this seems a little difficult to believe in the case of *Pteranodon*, which had a wing span of 27 feet.

The diet of pterosaurs presents an equally difficult problem. Their teeth were sharp and projected forward, as in many fish-eating animals, and they are usually found in marine deposits. However, they could not have dived for their prey, like a cormorant, for they would not have been able to take off again from the water. We must therefore guess that they glided sufficiently high above the sea to see the fish, and then swooped down to impale any that came close to the surface. The Cretaceous pterosaurs, or pterodactyls, had lost the tail and also reduced the number of teeth. In *Pterodactylus* the teeth are lost from the back parts of the jaws, but in *Dsungaripterus* they were instead lost from the front parts, which end in long sharp spikes. These, and the toothless jaws of the great *Pteranodon*, must have been used to spear fish.

All in all, the pterosaurs presented many unsolved problems as to their exact way of life, and it does not seem surprising that they were replaced by those more competent fliers, the birds, at the end of the Cretaceous.

Giant *Pteranodon* (*top*), 6 ins. long
Pterodactylus (*middle*) and
Dsungaripterus (*bottom*)

Back to the sea (I)

Life on land is much more demanding than life in the sea. Problems of body support and locomotion are more complex. The physical conditions such as temperature vary far more, and the abundance of food changes according to the season more than it does in the sea. But if an animal can cope with these conditions, it may be able to return to the sea and compete successfully with the more conservative animals which never left the sea. Three or four types of reptile have returned to the sea in this way, using both of the two basic

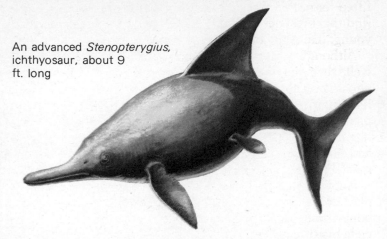

An advanced *Stenopterygius,*
ichthyosaur, about 9
ft. long

ways of swimming. In some the body and tail were flexed from side to side like those of a fish, while in others the limbs were used to row the body along.

Flexure of the body was used by the ichthyosaurs, which were common in the Jurassic and Cretaceous. They looked very like the modern porpoises, with a streamlined body that was obviously adapted for fast swimming. The limbs were reduced to short wide steering paddles. Specimens from the finely grained Lower Jurassic shales of Germany show that the body tapered gradually and then expanded into a fish-like tail, and that there was a dorsal fin.

The skeletons of young ichthyosaurs have also been found preserved within the body of some of the larger specimens, or projecting from it, presumably through the birth passage. The tail and small limbs of these ichthyosaurs were quite un-

Omphalosaurus, about
9 ft. long, a
Triassic ichthyo-
saur

fitted for use on the land and it is therefore not surprising to
find this evidence that the ichthyosaurs gave birth to living
young, like some of the water snakes today.

Although ichthyosaurs probably fed on a diet of fish as
well, their fossilized stomach contents often include many
remains of ammonaids. Related to the squids and cuttle-
fish, many of these creatures had a spiral shell from which
protruded the head and tentacles. Another different diet was
favored by a Triassic ichthyosaur, *Omphalosaurus,* which
had strongly built jaws and flattened crushing teeth and
must have fed on mollusks.

Another mollusk-eating aquatic group were the turtle-like
placodonts of the Triassic. Many of these had developed a
bony armor enclosing their short body, while the limbs
were modified into paddles for swimming. The skull is short
and powerful and, although most of them had large crushing
tooth plates, in others the teeth were replaced with a horny
turtle-like beak.

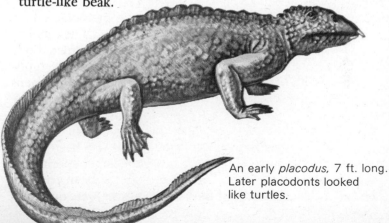

An early *placodus,* 7 ft. long.
Later placodonts looked
like turtles.

Back to the sea (II)

A group of marine reptiles that were as successful as the ichthyosaurs were the Jurassic and Cretaceous plesiosaurs. Unlike the ichthyosaurs, they rowed themselves along with powerful backward strokes of their expanded paddle-like limbs. This propulsive stroke must have been followed by a recovery stroke in which the paddle was rotated and brought forward edge first to reduce its resistance to the water, just as a modern oarsman 'feathers' his oar. Neither the short, rather rigid body, nor the fairly small tail seem to have been used to aid the paddles in swimming.

Two quite different types of plesiosaur can be distinguished, even in the Jurassic forms. *Pleiosaurus* itself, about 10 feet long, and its relatives, had small heads and very long necks. The most extreme form was 40-foot long *Elasmosaurus* of the Upper Cretaceous of North America, for its neck contained 76 vertebrae and was twice as long as its body. The paddles of these plesiosaurs were short and they were probably not very fast swimmers, catching their prey by the agility of their flexible neck rather than by their speed alone.

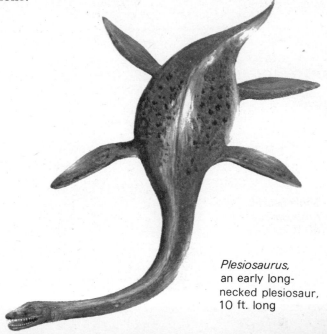

Plesiosaurus,
an early long-
necked plesiosaur,
10 ft. long

The other line of plesiosaurs, often called the pliosaurs, had longer paddles, a much shorter neck and a larger, more powerful head. *Kronosaurus* of the Lower Cretaceous of Australia, 40 feet long, had a head 12 feet long. The powerful jaws and greater size of the pliosaurs indicate that they preyed on larger marine life. Like those of ichthyosaurs, their fossilized stomach contents show that their diet included ammonoids, and they probably also preyed on ichthyosaurs and on the other plesiosaurs. Both lines of plesiosaur were common during the Upper Cretaceous, but then abruptly died out and are unknown in the succeeding rocks of the early Cenozoic era.

Two giant cretaceous plesiosaurs

Long-necked
elasmosaurus, 40 ft. long

Short-necked
Kronosaurus,
40 ft. long

Extinction — the great puzzle

For about 140 million years, from the Middle Triassic onward, the great adaptive radiations of the archosaurian and marine reptiles dominated this planet. Then, abruptly, at the end of the Cretaceous, the main reptilian groups disappeared forever from the land, the sea and the air. Of all the carnivorous and herbivorous saurischians, the bipedal and quadrupedal ornithischians, the pterosaurs, ichthyosaurs and plesiosaurs, none survived to compete with the little mammals that soon colonized the empty world.

To a vertebrate paleontologist, this dramatic event is the most fascinating problem of all. It is difficult to think of any single factor that could have been responsible for the extinction of such a variety of animals, living in such a variety of environments. It is probable that some of these extinctions were involved with others. For example, the carnivorous dinosaurs could not have survived the disappearance of their herbivorous relatives. Similarly, it is possible that the extinction of the ichthyosaurs and plesiosaurs might be connected with the disappearance of the Mesozoic types of cephalopod, the ammonoids in particular, that seem to have formed an important element in their diet. Even then, the problem of explaining the extinction of these cephalopods would remain.

In any case, there is an unusual feature in all these extinctions. The fossil record shows many examples of groups that gradually die out when a competing group becomes more common and diverse. Here, instead, the reptile groups disappeared suddenly and completely, when they were apparently at the peak of their success. Yet one cannot point to any new and expanding group as the cause of their eclipse. Although all these groups seem to have disappeared simultaneously, perhaps we must regard this as merely a coincidence, and attempt to find different explanations for the end of the different Mesozoic reptiles.

It has been suggested that the dinosaurs simply became too large, and therefore became extinct. Casts of the brain cavity show that the pituitary gland was very large. As this gland is responsible for the growth of the body, it has been suggested that for some reason it had become overactive, driving the dinosaurs to ever greater size. But the size of this gland is more likely a result of the large body size than its cause. In any case, moderate-sized dinosaurs did exist, but died out with their larger relatives.

Although they replaced the dinosaurs, the mammals do not seem to have been the cause of their extinction. Mammals first appeared in the Triassic, but were quite insignificant throughout the Mesozoic. None of them were larger than a cat, and they only increased in size and variety after the dinosaurs had disappeared. The puzzle here is to explain why the mammals seem to have fared so poorly in competition with the dinosaurs.

It is tempting to try to relate the extinction of the dinosaurs to any other changes that seem to have taken place during the Cretaceous. For example, it was a period of relatively intense geological activity, with many new mountain ranges rising. But these events must have been extremely gradual and local in their effects, while the dinosaurs disappeared in a fairly short space of time over all the earth's surface.

Another change in the Cretaceous was the gradual appearance of the type of vegetation that is familiar to us today, with forests of broad-leaved trees and conifers. But this change does not in fact seem to have had any great effect on the dinosaurs, for those of the Upper Cretaceous were already surviving in this more modern plant world without any apparent reduction in numbers or variety. Indeed, the hadrosaurs and ceratopsians were new Upper Cretaceous herbivores that apparently evolved to feed on these new plants.

As mentioned earlier (see pages 80 to 81) the dinosaurs may have depended on their large size in regulating their body temperature. We know, though, that they had no warm covering to insulate them, as birds and mammals have. A final possibility, then, is that the climate of the Cretaceous may gradually have become cooler, until the uninsulated dinosaurs could no longer keep a sufficiently high body temperature. But, even if the climate did become cooler, one would expect that dinosaurs would have been able to survive into the Cenozoic in the hotter, regions of the world.

The problem remains unsolved. Why did so many and diverse groups of reptiles disappear, so suddenly and simultaneously?

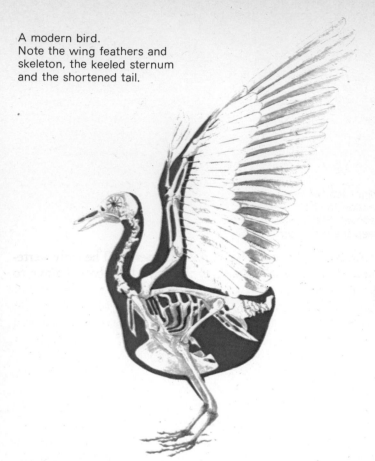

A modern bird.
Note the wing feathers and
skeleton, the keeled sternum
and the shortened tail.

Success in the air

In both pterosaurs and bats, flight evolved at the expense of
the ability to run on the ground. Even when folded, their
leathery wings are so cumbersome that bats must hang
upside down and can only drag themselves about awkward-
ly. Walking on its hind legs alone involves some difficulties
for the bird, whose bony tail is short and cannot balance the
weight of the body as did the tail of the bipedal reptiles.
The bird's body is therefore shortened and, by swinging the
femur downward and backward, the body is brought back
to lie over the hind limbs. The wing is supported mainly by
the enlarged bones of the third finger, and powerful flight
muscles are attached to the sides of a great keel that projects
downward from the sternum.

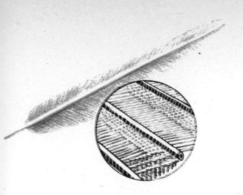
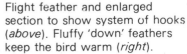

Flight feather and enlarged
section to show system of hooks
(*above*). Fluffy 'down' feathers
keep the bird warm (*right*).

Active flight uses a great deal of energy. The only vertebrates that have achieved it, the birds and the bats, belong to
groups whose physiology is advanced and that can control
their body temperature. Feathers, which evolved from the
scales that cover a reptile's body, keep birds warm and also
form the extremely light expanded surface needed for a
wing. This surface is made up of many tiny fibers that attach
to one another by a system of minute hooks. If these are torn
apart, the bird has only to stroke them together with its
beak, while preening, for them to interlock agaiin. The
feathers are replaced, in sequence, at least once a year.

Diagram of the chest of a bird to show the wing muscles. The
larger, outer muscle is attached to the lower surface of the humerus and pulls the wing down. The smaller, deeper muscle is
attached to the upper surface of the humerus and therefore pulls
the wing upward.

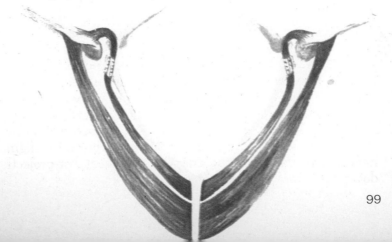

Archaeopteryx,
the first bird,
about the size
of a crow

The origin of birds

Archaeopteryx, from the late Jurassic, is one of the most
famous and significant fossils, for it is a perfect intermediate
stage between a reptile and a bird. The skeleton is similar to
that of an ornithischian dinosaur. The jaws still bear little
pointed teeth, and the bony tail is quite long. What is known
of the sternum shows little evidence of a bird-like keel for
flight muscles. Each finger was clawed, and although the
bones of the forearm and hand are elongated, the three fingers are quite separate and not fused as in a modern bird's
wings. Specimens of *Archaeopteryx* are preserved in the
shales of Solenhofen in Germany, which are so fine-grained
that clear impressions of the feathers can be seen. The fea-
thered wing was fully bird-like, although rather small, and
there was a row of feathers along each side of the long tail,
which may have been used in steering and gliding. *Archaeopteryx* was probably not a very powerful or skillful flier,
but it was clearly already a bird rather than a reptile.

Cretaceous toothed birds.

Ichthyornis, about the size of a tern

Hesperornis, a 3 ft. tall diving bird

Birds probably evolved from arboreal archosaurian reptiles that jumped from branch to branch. Many modern reptiles and mammals that do this can use a flap of skin along the sides of the body to extend their jump and cushion their landing. Like so many other archosaurs, the ancestral bird was probably mainly bipedal, so that the forearm was free for modification into a wing. The skeleton of a bird is so light and fragile that it is rarely preserved, but some marine chalk beds give a picture of bird life in the late Cretaceous. Naturally, these fossils are mainly remains of such sea-going birds such as our loons, grebes and pelicans. — for example *Ichthyornis,* 8 inches tall, may be an early gull. These beds also contain the remains of an extinct wingless bird, *Hesperornis,* which was nearly 3 feet tall and was primitive enough still to have teeth in part of its jaws. It had also lost all the bones of its wing except the humerus and, unlike the penguins, which have modified their wings into flippers, it must have used the hind limbs and out-turned feet for swimming.

101

Giant running birds

Relatively few birds actually catch their food while in flight. For most, flying is a useful way of escaping enemies and moving about quickly. There is no great reason to retain the power of flight when these enemies are absent, and flightless birds can instead develop long legs for fast running.

One group, known as the Ratites, were probably originally poor fliers like the tinamous, modern ratites from South America. This group developed into a variety of large running birds, often in islands or continents where active carnivores were absent or rare. The modern rhea of South America, the emu and cassowary of Australia, the ostrich of Asia and Africa and the little insectivorous kiwi of New

Extinct flightless carnivorous birds

Diatryma, 7 ft. tall, from North America

Phororhachos, 6 ft. tall, from South America

Zealand, are all living ratites. Two others, the 'elephant bird' *Aepyornis* of Madagascar and the 10 feet high moa of New Zealand, were probably only recently exterminated by man.

Most of the ratites are grazing herbivores, but two groups of giant flightless birds had large skulls with powerful beaks and must have been carnivores. *Diatryma,* 7 feet tall, from the Lower Eocene of North America and Europe, lived at a time when carnivorous mammals were quite small. Because it was an island in the Lower Tertiary, South America was still free from large active mammalian carnivores as late as the Pliocene, and a number of flightless carnivorous birds evolved, such as Miocene *Phororhachos,* 6 feet high and with a skull as large as that of a horse.

Modern ratites

Ostrich, from Africa

Rhea, from
South America

Emu, from
Australia

What is a mammal?

The mammals can be distinguished from normal reptiles in four important ways—in their control of their body temperature, in their method of development, in their intelligence and in their teeth.

Like the birds, mammals can keep their body temperature at a constant level and therefore can be equally active in cold climates and in hot. Heat is retained by their coating of hair. If the mammal should become too cold, heat is produced by rapid quivering or 'shivering' of the muscles, or alternatively if it becomes overheated, it loses heat by sweating.

Except for the monotremes (see pages 108 to 109), mammals do not lay eggs but instead produce living young that develop in the mother's uterus. In most mammals the embryo is attached to the wall of the uterus at a region called the placenta.

The blood systems of the embryo and its mother are separated by only a thin membrane. Through this membrane, food substances and oxygen diffuse from the mother's blood to that of the embryo, while the embryo's waste products diffuse into the mother's blood. After it is born, the young mammal will continue to receive nourishment from the mother, although at this time it is in the form of milk.

In placental mammals, such as ourselves, the whole period of development takes place in the uterus. In the marsupials (see pages 110 to 111), on the other hand, the embryo is born at a very early stage of development and crawls up into the

In most reptiles the air passes through the nose into the front end of the mouth,.and the cerebral hemispheres are small.

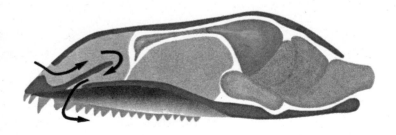

Molar tooth of a pig, showing the complicated pattern of crushing cusps.

mother's pouch. Once it is there it becomes attached to one of the mother's teats and continues to develop for several months.

Due mainly to its larger cerebral hemispheres, the brain of a mammal is much larger, in relation to its body, than that of a reptile. A mammal is capable of learning from past experience and modifying its instinctive reactions, its behavior being far less stereotyped than that of other vertebrates.

The teeth of a mammal are considerably more complicated than those of a reptile, for their crowns have a pattern of little cusps that are used to grind up the food. A bony hard palate separates the mouth of a mammal from its air passage so that its food, while it is in the process of being chewed, does not in any way interfere with its breathing.

In mammals air passes into the back of the mouth and the cerebral hemispheres are very large.

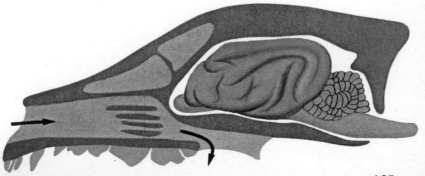

The origin of mammals

The change from a mammal-like reptile, or synapsid (see pages 62 to 63), was not sudden. Over many millions of years, the synapsids must gradually have become more mammalian in appearance, and advanced synapsids probably had a warm, furry body. Unfortunately, of the differences between a reptile and a mammal, only the structure of the teeth is directly visible in a fossil—and some of the advanced synapsids have cheek teeth with cusps, like those of primitive mammals. However, one skeletal difference between the two groups is that reptiles have several bones in the lower jaw, while mammals have only one. This feature is therefore used as a convenient, though arbitrary, method of distinguishing between the two groups. There is yet no clear series of animals linking a particular synapsid, such as a cynodont or tritylodont, with the earliest known mammals. This is probably because the early mammals were little animals, whose remains would not readily have been fossilized. This gap is slowly being filled by modern discoveries and study.

Many of the little early mammals are known only by their teeth and jaws. One of the earliest known is a shrew-like creature, *Morgonucodon,* from the Upper Triassic of Great Britain. Like several other Jurassic and Cretaceous mammals, it seems to have fed on insects and other invertebrates. One Upper Jurassic group, known as the pantotheres, were

Morganucodon, about 4 ins. long. One of the first mammals.

Taeniolabis, 4 ft. long. A Paleocene multituberculate

probably ancestral to both modern marsupials and placentals. The first herbivorous mammals were the multituberculates, with teeth like those of modern rodents, with strong incisors and wide, chewing molars. The Mesozoic multituberculates like *Ctenacodon* were quite small, but in the Paleocene, after the dinosaurs had disappeared, such forms as *Taeniolabis* were the size of a small pig.

There are about thirty main groups of Cenozoic mammals, and we shall deal only with those that include particularly interesting fossils. Several familiar groups are omitted, such as the carnivores, rodents, insectivores, rabbits and bats.

Head of *Ctenacodon,* an early multituberculate

The eggs of a platypus
are laid at the end of a
long burrow which
winds to the riverbank.

Egg-laying mammals

Australia has been cut off from land connections with the rest of the world since at least the end of the Cretaceous. Primitive types of mammal have therefore been able to survive there, protected from the competition of more advanced mammals. The marsupials of Australia are well known, but the continent also shelters two even more primitive mammals, the platypus and the echidna, the only members of a group known as the monotremes.

The most surprising characteristic of the monotremes is that they do not produce living young, as do all other mammals. Instead, they lay eggs, which are very similar to those produced by reptiles, and then incubated by the parents.

108

When these eggs hatch, the young are nourished by milk oozing from skin glands inside a pouch on the mother's belly. Although the monotremes are covered with hair, their control over their body temperature is not as efficient as that of other mammals.

The skeleton of the monotremes is also very primitive in several ways. For example, the pectoral girdle is considerably less advanced than that of the Triassic mammal-like reptiles. It is quite possible that the monotremes evolved, from the synapsids, independently of the line that led to the other

Australian spiny anteater, *Echidna,* about 3 ft. long. Other closely related anteaters live in New Guinea.

mammals. Unfortunately the teeth, which might well have provided a clue to their evolution, are absent and their fossil history is unknown.

Both the platypus and the echidna are very specialized types. The platypus is aquatic and has webbed feet, and feeds on invertebrates from the beds of streams. Its snout has become a duck-like bill, within which are a number of crushing horny tooth plates. The echidna is covered with sharp spines similar to those of a hedgehog. Its powerful limbs and claws are used to tear open the nests of ants or termites, and its long toothless snout encloses a long sticky tongue that the animal uses to catch insects.

109

Marsupials

The young marsupial is born at a very early stage of development—only eight days after conception in the American
opossum. It is still very small, that of a five-foot high kangaroo being only one inch long. Even at this stage, its forelimbs are developed so that it can crawl up the mother's
belly to the pouch.

Although Australia is the main home of the marsupials
today, they are known from early Tertiary deposits in Europe and the American continents. These early marsupials
seem to have been very like the living opossums which are

Opossum

arboreal, omnivorous or insectivorous. The opossums are
exceptional in being able to compete successfully with the
placental mammals, for they are still spreading northward
in the United States. Most marsupials seem only to have
flourished in continents which were isolated from the later-
evolving and more advanced placental carnivores.

The South American marsupials took advantage of the
absence of these carnivores to become carnivores themselves,
preying on the primitive ungulate and edentate placentals
that occupied herbivorous ways of life (see pages 124 to
127). *Borhyaena* of the Miocene was rather like a modern
wolf, and *Thylacosmilus* of the Pliocene had long stabbing
upper canine teeth, like the saber-toothed cats. Both the
marsupial carnivores and their primitive ungulate prey became extinct in the late Tertiary, when the more advanced

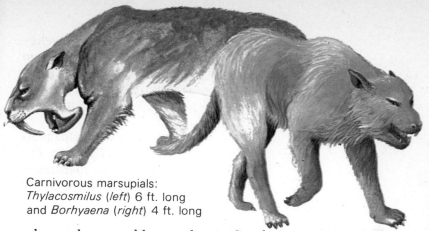

Carnivorous marsupials:
Thylacosmilus (*left*) 6 ft. long
and *Borhyaena* (*right*) 4 ft. long

placentals were able to colonize South America by the re-established Panama Isthmus.

Unfortunately, the history of the Australian marsupials is almost unknown, for hardly any fossils earlier than the Pleistocene have been found. In addition to wolf-like, mole-like and ant-eating forms, the main radiation has been into a great variety of herbivores. Apart from the lumbering 11 feet long *Diprotodon* of the Pleistocene, all the fossils belong to types that are still alive today. The grazing bipedal kangaroos and wallabies are probably the most unusual of these herbivores. Some extinct Pleistocene kangaroos, such as the short-faced *Sthenurus,* were about seven feet tall.

Australian Ice Age marsupials.
Diprotodon (*left*) and *Sthenurus* (*right*)

Characteristics of herbivores

Life is, in some ways, much easier for carnivores than herbivores. Although the carnivore's food has first to be caught, it can then be easily eaten. Meat has a high energy value and it is easy to digest. A herbivore must have a large body so that its food can be retained long enough for the bacteria of its intestine to digest the cellulose walls of the plant cells. The dentition must also be adapted to cope with the large quantities of silica-containing vegetation the animal must eat, which tends to wear the teeth away. The cheek teeth of a herbivore are therefore usually widened and lengthened to increase their area, with a complicated pattern of ridges on the crown of the tooth. This is also greatly deepened so that it will stand up to a longer period of grinding before it is worn down to the root and useless. The snout and jaw become very deep to accommodate these teeth.

By the evolution of longer limbs herbivores were able to escape from their predators. This increase of speed was achieved by elongating some of the bones and by walking on the tips of the toes, each of which became capped by a horny hoof. These changes in teeth and limbs took place in nearly all the herbivorous placentals, called the ungulates, but they are known particularly well in the horses (see pages 120 to 121). Very early stages can be seen in three types of primitive ungulate from the Eocene and Oligocene of the

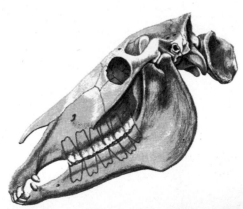

Ridges on the crown of a horse's molar tooth (*above*) and their deep roots (*right*)

United States. The most primitive was *Phenacodus*, 5½ feet long, which had tiny hoofs but still had a long low skull and teeth which were only poorly adapted for grinding. *Coryphodon* was about 8 feet long and much more heavily built, with teeth that were widened but still not deepened. The largest was *Uintatherium*, which had bony projections on top of its skull. Its heavy body was carried by short powerful limbs and wide feet.

Archaic hoofed mammals:
Uintatherium,
about 12 ft. long

Coryphodon,
about 8 ft. long

Phenacodus, about
6 ft. long

Unusual ungulates

Arsinoitherium, from the Lower Oligocene of Egypt, was a large rhinoceros-like herbivore, which does not seem closely related to any other ungulate. The heavy body was supported by strongly built limbs and broad feet. The head bore a pair of massive horns. Egypt was also, in the Eocene period, the home of the earliest members of the Sirenia, or sea-cows, a peculiar group of aquatic mammals. Two sirenians are known today, the Pacific dugong and the Atlantic manatees, which are all about 10 feet long.

Another peculiar primitive ungulate was *Desmostylus,* 7½ feet long, which lived in the coastal waters of the northern Pacific in the mid-Tertiary. Unlike the other sirenians, its limbs were powerful and the jaws bore strong protruding tusks, suggesting that it may have eaten mollusks, prising them off the rocks.

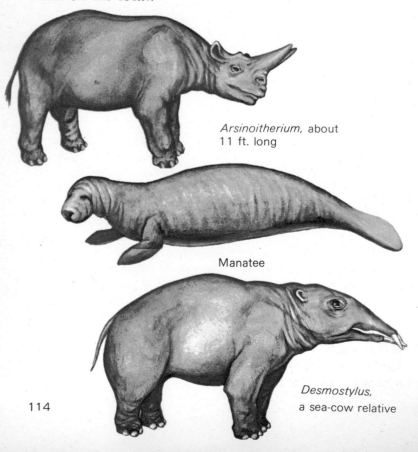

Arsinoitherium, about 11 ft. long

Manatee

Desmostylus, a sea-cow relative

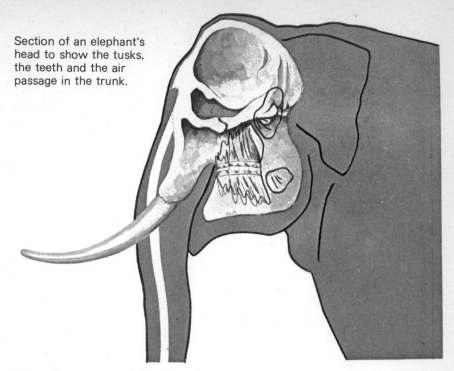

Section of an elephant's head to show the tusks, the teeth and the air passage in the trunk.

The adaptations of elephants

The herbivore's problem of eating enough food without wearing out its teeth is even more acute in a large animal. As it becomes larger, its weight and food requirements increase more rapidly than the area of its tooth surface. Elephants eventually solved this problem by using the teeth in turn. Each tooth is very deep, with folded transverse ridges of enamel on its surface. Only four teeth are usually visible at any given time, one in each half of each jaw. As a tooth is worn down, it is pushed out of the front of the jaw by the next tooth, which moves forward to replace it. There are no anterior teeth other than the large tusks.

The elephant's body is supported by pillar-like limbs, ending in round feet. The limbs cannot support the weight if they are bent more than a little. Because the heavy head would be difficult to support if the neck were long, the neck is shortened. The mouth then cannot reach the ground and food is instead taken in by the upper lip, now elongated into a strong muscular trunk.

The evolution of elephants

There are four main groups of elephants.

Dinotheres were a very distinct line that survived almost unchanged from the Miocene to the final Pleistocene species, which reached a height of 10 feet high at the shoulder. The dinotheres used all their low-crowned cheek teeth at once. They had no upper tusks, but their large lower tusks were curved downward and backward, and they probably had quite a long trunk.

Phiomia of the Egyptian Oligocene is the earliest representative of the line to all other elephants. About 4 feet high at the shoulder, *Phiomia* had a well-developed trunk, and tusks in both upper and lower jaws. The cheek teeth were low-crowned but elongated. As they were all in use at the same time, the jaws were lengthened to accommodate them. These long-jawed forms were extremely successful and very varied in the late Tertiary, but only a few survived into the Pleistocene. *Gomphotherium,* which lived during the Miocene was only 6 feet high at the shoulder and had a very long snout and lower jaw, although probably a rather short trunk.

Short-jawed mastodonts still had low-crowned teeth but, as they used only two teeth at a time in each half of each jaw, they were able to shorten the jaw. They had lost the lower tusks, but the upper tusks were still very large. Known from the Miocene onward, these animals culminated in the Pleistocene *Mammut* that was found in Africa, Eurasia and North America, and which survived until about 6000 B.C.

Modern elephants, of which there are only two kinds, are the end of a line which is known first in the Miocene. Their deepened teeth and shortened jaws have already been described (see page 115). Typical elephants as we know them appeared in the Pleistocene and extinct relatives of the living African elephant varied in size from 14 feet at the shoulder, to elephants the size of pigs, from the Mediterranean islands. The Pleistocene mammoths, *Mammuthus,* are related to the living Indian elephant. These were long tusked and they included the woolly mammoths, adapted to the cold of the Ice Ages, whoses carcasses have been found in the frozen soil of Siberia and Alaska.

Woolly mammoth (*Mammuthus*)

Mastodon (*Mammut*)

Gomphotherium

Phiomia

Dinotherium

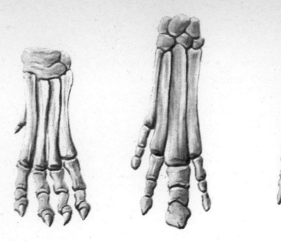

(A) Forefoot of dog (B) perissodactyl or 'odd-toe' and (C) artio-dactyl or 'even-toe'

Odd-toes and even-toes

Nearly all the fast-moving advanced herbivores of the later Tertiary belonged to one or other of two groups of ungulates. Like many running animals, they greatly lengthened their limbs by elongating the five metacarpals or metatarsals (see page 35). If all five of these bones were elongated, the feet would be bulky and heavy. To lighten the limb without weakening it, the number of metacarpals and metatarsals was progressively reduced.

In one group, the perissodactyls, the weight-bearing axis of the limb passes through the middle toe, and this is ultimately the only toe left in some forms. There is, therefore, a single hoof on each limb of perissodactyls, such as horses.

In the other group, the artiodactyls, the limb axis passes between the third and fourth toes. These both remain in advanced artiodactyls, although their metacarpals or metatarsals may be fused together. Each limb therefore ends in a pair of hoofs—the 'cloven hoof' of pigs, camels, cattle, deer and giraffes.

These slightly different types of elongated specialized limb are just one example of many features which appear independently in both the perissodactyls and the artiodactyls. As both have evolved into fast-running herbivores, their similar ways of life have resulted in the appearance of many similar adaptations in the two groups, a process known as parallel evolution.

Giant rhinos

The living tapir is very like the earliest perissodactyls and is closely related to the rhinoceros. Known since the Oligocene, rhinoceroses started as small, light, running types, many later on developing horns made of fused hair-like material. Extinct rhinos include a variety of forms, the most spectacular being *Baluchitherium* from the Oligocene of Asia, which is the largest known land mammal. Its body, 18 feet high at the shoulder and carried on massive limbs, allowed the 4 feet long head to browse on the higher branches of trees.

Though not as enormous, the titanotheres of the early Tertiary were also large perissodactyls, *Brontotherium* of the Oligocene being 8 feet high at the shoulder.

Perhaps the most peculiar perissodactyl is *Moropus* of the Miocene. Although in general it looked like a clumsy version of a horse, the limbs end in large claws. *Moropus* presumably fed on roots that it dug up.

Baluchitherium,
a rhino

Brontotherium, a titanothere

Moropus, a chalicothere

Horses

The history of horses is understood better than that of any other group of mammal. This is because the North American Tertiary deposits contain a very good fossil series from the open grasslands where much of their evolution took place. The evolution illustrates clearly all the linked changes in size and in the structure of the limbs, teeth and skull that have already been outlined (see pages 112 to113), and some of these are shown opposite. One of the most important features of this evolution was that the relative size and complexity of the brain also increased in horses. The modern horse has considerable learning ability, and an elaborate system of communication, involving ears, tail and lips as well as sounds.

Horse evolution started with the little terrier-sized *Eohippus* of the Lower Eocene, which probably lived in forests, browsing on the leaves of trees and bushes. Although other genera from the later Eocene had slightly enlarged front cheek teeth, the first major advance appears in *Miohippus* of the Lower Oligocene. About the size of a sheep, it had three digits in each limb, and, although still mainly a forest browser, nearly all its cheek teeth were enlarged.

In the Lower Miocene, expanses of open grassland appeared in North America. Pony-sized *Parahippus,* which lived at this time, had a foot that was better adapted for rapid running on these plains, for the side toes were so reduced that they would not have touched the ground when running. The later Miocene genus, *Merychippus,* progressed a stage further in adapting to this life. Its teeth were deeper and better able to resist the abrasive power of grass. Along with the evolution of these grazing types, other horses (both small and large) remained three-toed forest dwellers.

Horse evolution after the Miocene merely consisted of the completion of these trends in teeth and limbs. From *Merychippus* to Pliocene *Pliohippus,* with tiny splint-like side toes, the line of descent continued to the modern horse *Equus,* in which these little bones have been lost altogether. *Equus* probably evolved in North America but soon spread to all continents except Australia.

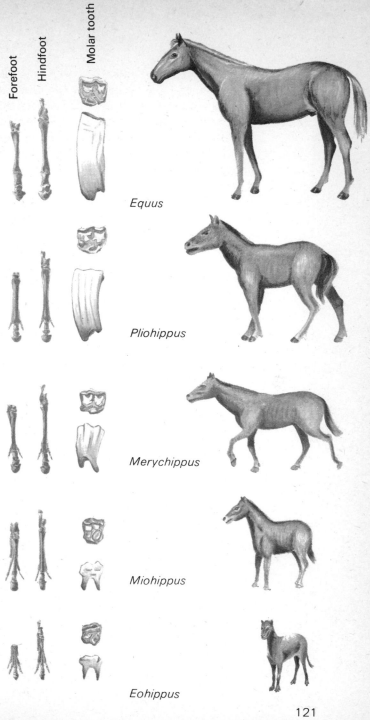

Forefoot

Hindfoot

Molar tooth

Equus

Pliohippus

Merychippus

Miohippus

Eohippus

121

Cloven hoofs

The artiodactyls include most of the hoofed mammals of today, and make up most of the herds of browsing and grazing herbivores still to be seen in Africa, but which were more common in the late Tertiary. Their great success is due mainly to the evolution of a very specialized system for obtaining and digesting plant food. The most remarkable part of the artiodactyl's digestive system is its stomach which is divided into several chambers. When first swallowed, the food enters the first chamber or 'rumen' where it is mixed with mucus, and bacteria break up and digest even the cellulose walls of the plant cells and reduce the food to a pulp. This 'cud' is then returned to the mouth and chewed thoroughly before it again descends, passing through the rumen to the other chambers of the stomach, where digestion continues. This allows the advanced artiodactyls, or 'ruminants' to spend little time on the exposed grasslands obtaining their food, and then return to a safer place to chew and digest it undistrubed.

The earliest forest-living artiodactyls of the Eocene were very similar to the living pig and hippopotamus, which still

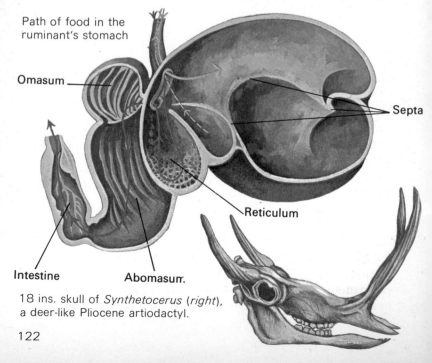

Path of food in the ruminant's stomach

Omasum

Septa

Reticulum

Intestine

Abomasum.

18 ins. skull of *Synthetocerus* (*right*), a deer-like Pliocene artiodactyl.

Alticamelus, a giraffe camel

Archaeotherium, a giant
pig-like artiodactyl.

show only the beginnings of the artiodactyl specializations of the limbs and stomach, and have low-crowned teeth. Even in the Oligocene, giant pig-like forms such as *Archaeotherium,* about 3 feet high, had smaller digits than the living pigs. One of the most distinct groups of ruminants includes the camels and llamas. Common since the Eocene, the hoofs have been replaced by nails and large pads beneath the toes. The group includes the giraffe-like forms of the Miocene and Pliocene, such as 10 feet tall *Alticamelus.*

From the Miocene onward, the great radiation of artiodactyls have been the dominant herbivorous mammals. Many have stabbing canines or permanent or temporary bony projections on their skulls for defense. These projections may be permanent and horn-covered, like those of antelope and cattle, or may be bare bony antlers, replaced each year as in deer.

Thoatherium, the South American equivalent of the horse.

Pseudo-horses and others

Throughout the main land masses of North America, Eurasia and Africa, the more primitive types of herbivorous placental animals became extinct, due to competition from the more progressive perissodactyls and artiodactyls, with their highly evolved limbs and teeth. South America, however, was cut off from the rest of the world by the severing of the Panama Isthmus, soon after the archaic ungulates and edentates (see pages 126 to 127) had reached the continent in the Paleocene. Protected in this island continent, the early ungulates underwent an adaptive radiation of their own. It is interesting to find that this radiation produced animals similar to those resulting from the herbivore radiations taking place in the rest of the world. They provide a clear demonstration of 'convergent evolution'— whereby natural selection, continually modifying species so that they are adapted to their environment, operates in the same way, independently, in stocks only distantly related to one other. In fact, it was the examination of fossil remains of these South American animals in 1834 that first made Darwin realize how closely structure and environment are interrelated, and so eventually led to his theory of natural selection (see pages 8 to 9).

Perhaps the most remarkable of these parallels is the similarity between horses and some members of a South American group called the litopterns. *Thoatherium* of the Miocene, about the size of a collie dog, looked exactly like a small pony. Another type of litoptern, *Macrauchenia* of the Pliocene, was very camel-like in size and proportions, but may also have had a short elephant-like trunk. An even closer parallel to the elephants can be found in the heavily built *Pyrotherium,* which was very similar to the early ele-

124

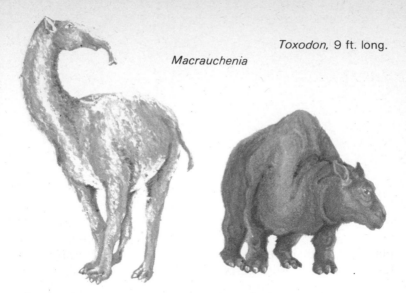

Macrauchenia

Toxodon, 9 ft. long.

phant *Phiomia* in its trunk, tusks and teeth. Another unrelated large herbivore was *Toxodon*.

Competition, leading to extinction and replacement, can be seen even within these South American ungulates. *Pyrotherium* is found only in the Oligocene. Earlier relatives of *Toxodon* flourished in the Miocene but few survived into the Pliocene. Most of the remaining South American forms became extinct toward the end of the Pliocene, when the re-establishment of the Panama Isthmus allowed the more progressive North American placentals to enter. Only *Toxodon* and *Macrauchenia* survived into the Pleistocene, but disappeared before the end of that period.

Pyrotherium, about 12 ft. long, an elephant-like South American mammal

Giant armadillos and sloths

Alongside the primitive ungulates of South America lived another early placental group, the edentates. Although the armadillos, anteaters and sloths are the only survivors, their earlier relatives included some remarkable giants. The omnivorous armadillos are known as early as the Paleocene of South America. The bony armor that covers the upper surface of the body, and often the head and tail, is divided into rings between the shoulder and hips. Although living armadillos are comparatively small, one Pleistocene genus was as large as a rhinoceros.

The glyptodonts, which appeared in the Eocene, were closely related to the armadillos. Their armor plates were closely joined into a toroise-like carapace supported by the fused vertebrae. Bony rings, and sometimes spikes, armed the tail. The last and largest of these herbivores was *Glyptodon* of the Pleistocene, which was about 9 feet long.

The tree sloths are in fact unknown as fossils, but their extinct relatives the ground sloths are sufficiently remark-

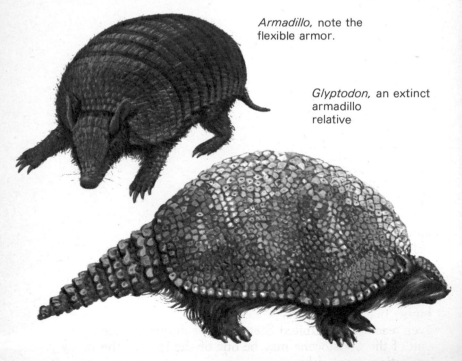

Armadillo, note the flexible armor.

Glyptodon, an extinct armadillo relative

Tree sloth, in its normal upside-down position. *Megatherium*, a giant Ice Age ground sloth.

able. Known from the Oligocene onward, these herbivores browsed on the leaves of trees and bushes whose branches they caught and pulled down with their strong claws. They must have moved very clumsily, for the feet are twisted over so that their weight was borne by the outer edge. Early ground sloths were only a few feet long, but the 20 foot long *Megatherium* of the Pleistocene was as large as an elephant and must have weighed several tons. Its great basin-like pelvis suggests that it may have sat back on its haunches like an enormous bear when at rest.

Unlike the South American ungulates, the ground sloths competed successfully with the invading North American higher placentals, for they flourished in the Pleistocene and even reached the United States. Their disappearance at the end of the Pleistocene may be one of the first of the many extinctions caused by man.

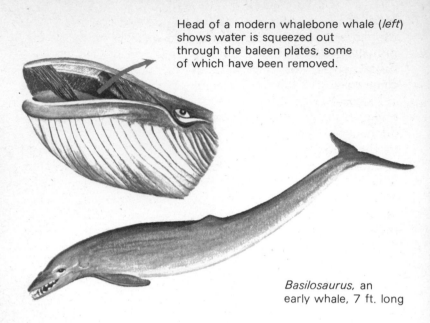

Head of a modern whalebone whale (*left*) shows water is squeezed out through the baleen plates, some of which have been removed.

Basilosaurus, an early whale, 7 ft. long

Whales

Life in the open sea is more difficult for a mammal than for a reptile, for it must develop a thick insulating covering to retain its body heat. The thick layer of oily fat, or 'blubber', serves this purpose in whales. Whales have lost the flexible neck of most mammals and developed a streamlined body like most other aquatic vertebrates. Unlike reptiles, that move by bending their bodies from side to side, the main flexibility of a mammal's body is up and down and the flukes of a whale's tail, which provide the swimming thrust, are horizontal. The front limbs are short steering flippers.

Freed, by the buoyancy of sea water, from having to support the weight of their body, whales were already large in the Eocene. *Basilosaurus,* for example, was about 70 feet long and its teeth were compressed and serrated, unlike the peglike teeth of modern fish-eating toothed whales. The largest whales are toothless and do not eat fish, but instead feed on tiny floating invertebrate animals — the gullet of even a 150-ton blue whale is only 9 inches across. The food is caught on a hair-like fringe around the edges of horny 'baleen' plates which hang from the roof of the mouth and is licked off by the huge tongue.

Man: the beginning

Monkeys, apes and man all belong in a group known as the primates. Also included are the lemurs, tarsiers and bush babies, small tree-living animals that are the almost unchanged descendants of the earliest primates.

Many features of the primates can be traced back to their origin in the trees. The abilities to reach out in a variety of directions and to grasp objects both evolved as adaptations to climbing. Such a life also requires the ability to judge accurately the size of objects and how far away they are. This can be achieved only if the fields of vision of the two eyes overlap to give binocular or 'stereoscopic' vision. The sense of smell is far less useful in the trees, and vision is therefore overwhelmingly important. The quickness and degree of muscular coordination needed for arboreal life also demands considerable development of the brain. The characteristic skull shape is also the result of these habits. The reduction of the sense of smell, and the number of cheek teeth, led to a shortening of the muzzle, and the eyes moved around to the front of the skull until their fields of vision overlapped. The progressive enlargement of the braincase is the most characteristic feature of the primates, whose success is due to the interplay of brain, eyes and and hands to achieve things beyond the capabilities of other animals.

Ring-tailed *Lemur*.
All the lemurs
live in Madagascar

Tarsier, their
huge eyes aid in
night hunting

129

Ateles, South American
spider monkey

Rhesus monkey,
an Old World monkey

Man's relatives

The breeding period, when the female is receptive to the
male, is restricted in most animals. The fact that, in advanced primates, the sexual cycle recurs regularly about
every month has had far reaching effects on their evolution,
and the continuing attraction between the sexes is the basis
of the complex social life. The social unit varies but the
social life has led to the development of an elaborate system
of communication, based partly on sounds and partly on the
signalling of emotions, using the complex face musculature.
Within the protection of the family and community, the
young primate has a long training period and nearly all its
behavioral patterns are learned, not instinctive.

Apart from certain specializations, there is little basic
difference between monkeys and a primitive primate such
as a tarsier. In fact, there is little doubt that the South
American monkeys and the Old World monkeys are two independent lines, each of which evolved in the Eocene from
a tarsier-like ancestor. Both lines are mainly arboreal, and in
the South American monkeys such as *Ateles* the tail is prehensile too. They also differ from their Old World cousins in
having hair on their faces and nostrils which are further apart.

Baboon, a ground dweller

Chimpanzee

The Old World monkeys, apes and man all belong to a single evolutionary stock. The early members were probably very like the modern rhesus and vervet monkeys—living in trees and feeding omnivorously on fruit, berries, insects, lizards and other small animals. Other living monkeys, such as the baboons, have become ground dwellers, walking on all fours, with the palms of their hands flat on the ground. They have long dog-like muzzles.

Size and its consequences are the main differences between the apes and monkeys. The larger apes do not walk, like monkeys, along the tree branches but swing from branch to branch using their long, powerfully muscled arms, which are longer than their legs. There is no external sign of their tail. The methods of communication and the social organization of the apes are particularly well developed. A chimpanzee, for example, can express itself using over thirty sounds and a variety of facial expressions, and it has an efficient memory. Like the various nationalities of man, different groups of chimpanzees have different social traditions.

The evolution of man

Man himself did not of course evolve from an ape, but apes and man diverged from a common ancestral group, the apes remaining in the trees while man became an erect terrestrial biped. *Dryopithecus* (also known as *Proconsul*) of the Miocene and early Pliocene of Africa, Europe and southern Asia was probably close to that common ancestor in its structure and habits. The limbs of *Dryopithecus,* which was about the size of a chimpanzee, show some signs of the ability to brachiate, but the feet also show a trend toward a bipedal posture. This mixture of characters may be due to its environment of woodland and of open grassland across which it would have had to run.

After this, the story of man's evolution is mainly a matter of the gradual increase in the size of the brain and the development of a fully upright posture. The next fossil on the path to man is *Australopithecus,* who lived in caves in Africa and Asia during the Lower Pleistocene. *Australopithecus* stood upright but had a brain capacity only slightly larger than that of living apes.

The characteristic used to define man himself, *Homo,* is the ability to make tools. The earliest remains that can confidently be accepted as belonging to man are from the Middle Pleistocene, about 500,000 years ago. These creatures, called *Homo erectus* (originally named *Pithecanthropus*) were familiar with both fire and pottery, and have been found in Java, China, Africa, and Europe. *Homo erectus* lived during the second of the four great Ice Ages that brought glaciers southward across North America and Eurasia. It was not until the Third Ice Age, from about 70,000 years ago, that a species of man became common. Several different types of this species, *Homo neanderthalensis,* are known. The one most common in Europe had quite a large brain case, but the skull was rather long and low, and there were prominent brow ridges. These specialized characteristics contrast with the high-vaulted brain case of modern man, *Homo sapiens.* Their early history before the end of the last Ice Age, about 25,000 years ago, is still uncertain. Early members of the species, known as Cro-Magnon man, arrived in western Europe at that time and, in true *Homo sapiens* fashion, seem to have wiped out their relatives, the Neanderthals.

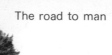

The road to man

Dryopithecus, ancestral to both apes and man

Australopithecus, fully upright but small brained

Homo erectus, the first true man

Homo neanderthalensis, an early widespread, cold adapted species

Cro-Magnon man, no different from modern Homo sapiens

CHANGING SCENES OF LIFE

In the following pages, the appearance of the world and its faunas in each of the periods from the Devonian onward will be reconstructed. Maps illustrate the main areas where vertebrate fossils of the period are found. Older rocks have suffered more from the destructive force of erosion and have been covered by a greater variety of later deposits. The areas where these older rocks are still to be found outcropping at the surface are therefore more restricted than the outcrops of younger rocks.

Devonian forest scene including the amphibian *Ichthyostega*

The Devonian Period
(395 to 345 million years ago)
This is the fourth period of the Paleozoic Era. Most of the primitive ostracoderms and placoderms are found only in the Devonian. Their short history is due to the appearance of more advanced fish, for all the major groups had appeared by the close of the period. Sharks such as *Cladoselache* and a few bony ray-finned fish such as *Cheirolepis* existed with

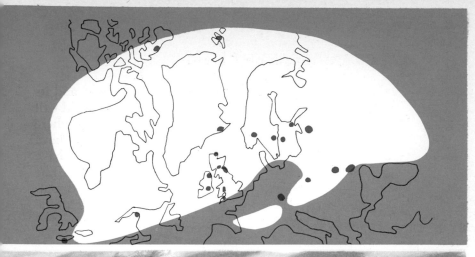

Devonian fresh-water fish

some early lobe-finned fish and rhipidistians.

Most of the Devonian fossils are found in high northern latitudes. These areas probably lay much further to the south in the Devonian, for many of these deposits are red sandstones that may have been laid down in warm conditions with seasonal droughts and torrential rains. Measurements of fossil magnetism suggest that these continents were even south of the equator at that time, and also show that North America and Europe were adjacent to one another.

Devonian marine fauna

The Carboniferous Period
(345 to 280 million years ago)
This period is named after the coal layers common in its later deposits. It is often subdivided into the Pennsylvanian period and the older Mississippian period, in which the rocks are mainly marine limestones.

The archaic ostracoderm and placoderm fish of the Devonian had disappeared completely. The marine fauna was dominated by the cartilaginous fish, including both shark-like forms and bottom dwellers similar to the later skates and rays. A fresh-water fauna lived in the swamps, in which the Pennsylvanian coal deposits were laid down, and was dominated by the bony fish. The lobe-finned fish were no longer common, and a host of ray-finned chondrosteans are instead found in nearly all these deposits.

Amphibians were, for the first time, common in the coal swamps. As would be expected in such an environment, most of them were fish-eaters that spent most or all of their lives in the water. The labyrinthodont amphibians included both temnospondyls and embolomeres, and several types of small aquatic lepospondyl also existed.

Little is known of the land vertebrates of the Carboniferous but, since the ancestors of both the synapsid and the diapsid reptiles had appeared early in the Pennsylvanian, the reptiles as a whole must have evolved even earlier.

The coal deposits of the Pennsylvanian were formed by the accumulation of the remains of huge fast-growing trees, living in a moist, mild, humid climate. The scale-trees *Lepidodendron* and *Sigillaria* were about 100 feet high and had trunks 4 to 6 feet in diameter. *Calamites* looked very like the living horsetails but was 30 to 35 feet high. The smaller vegetation of the swamps included ferns, and primitive conifer trees are found on higher, drier ground.

Nearly all the Carboniferous fossils are found in eastern North America and southern Europe. These areas seem to have moved into warmer latitudes, subtropical regions of high rainfall, but much of the continents of Gondwanaland (see page 20) lay around the South Pole and were covered by glaciers.

Carboniferous forest with amphibian (*right*)

The Permian Period
(280 to 225 million years ago)

The fish faunas of this period were very like those of the Carboniferous, although a single holostean in the late Permian is the forerunner of change in the Triassic.

The land fauna of the Lower Permian is best known from the Red Beds of Texas, which seem to have been laid down in the delta of a great river. Much of this fauna, including both labyrinthodont amphibians and primitive types of synapsid reptile, was aquatic or semiaquatic and must have included fish that were eaten by these tetrapods. Some terrestrial types of labyrinthodont, that reached their peak of evolution at this time, are also formed. Terrestrial reptiles included little lizard-like *Captorhinus* and the first land herbivores, the caseids.

The record of land life in the Middle and Upper Permian is best preserved in South Africa and Russia. Only a few labyrinthodonts still survived, and most of these were aquatic. Soon after the Middle Permian the synapsid radiation achieved the first completely land-based tetrapod fauna, including both carnivores and the herbivores that provided their food.

After the swamps of the Carboniferous and the deltaic deposits of the lower Permian, the later Permian rocks of North America and Europe indicate an even drier, perhaps even desert, environment, suggesting that the northward

Lower Permian scene in Texas with *Eryops.*

movement of these continents had now taken them beyond the equatorial region of heavy rainfall. The scale-trees, *Calamites,* and ferns were able to survive only in local areas where the temperature was still mild. Many new mountain ranges appeared, and conifers were common on this higher, cooler ground.

The southern (Gondwanaland) continents also seem to have been moving northward, for their climate shows a progressive warming from the glaciers of the Lower Permian to warm swamplands at the end of the period. Although their flora is unlike that of the northern (Laurasian) continents, the two super-continents must still have been connected, as similar synapsid reptiles are found in South Africa and Eurasia.

Upper Permian scene in South Africa with mammal-like reptiles.

The Triassic Period
(225 to 195 million years ago)
This period, which marks the beginning of the Mesozoic era, was by far the most eventful period in the history of the vertebrates. In the fresh waters, as well as in the seas and on land, many far-reaching changes in vertebrate faunas took place.

The most important of the changes in the fish faunas was the rise of the more advanced holostean type of ray-finned fish. They not only replaced the more primitive chondrosteans in the fresh water but also, by spreading to the seas, were probably responsible for a considerable reduction in the variety of cartilaginous fish during the Triassic period.

Although the final result of the faunal changes on land was the complete replacement of the synapsid reptiles by the archosaurs, this took place in two stages. The archosaurs were primarily carnivorous, and it was the carnivorous synapsids that first disappeared, few surviving into the Triassic. During the Middle and Upper Triassic, in fact, the herbivorous cynodonts and dicynodonts were accompanied by a new group of lepidosaurian herbivores, that were known as the rhynchosaurs.

It was not until late in the Triassic that the last of the more archaic reptile groups finally disappeared and were replaced by the first of the early herbivorous dinosaurs, such as the prosauropods and ornithischians. Although the archosaur radiation was to last for approximately 130 million years, their successors had, however, already appeared, for the earliest known mammal was discovered in late Triassic rocks.

The Triassic was also the beginning of the reptile invasion of the waters. The phytosaurs and earliest crocodiles lived in the fresh water and probably were the cause of the extinction of the last of the labyrinthodont amphibians, which were also aquatic. By the end of the Triassic, the pliytosaurs had disappeared also.

Another group, which was at least partially aquatic, was the tortoise-like placodonts, which are found only in late Triassic deposits. Finally, early members of both the really successful types of marine reptile, the ichthyosaurs and the plesiosaurs, appeared during the Triassic.

The Triassic rocks of both North America and Europe are

again desert deposits, and the climate of South Africa had also become hot and dry by the end of the period, Upland areas supported conifer trees, which were over 100 feet high, and palm trees. Barrel-trunked cycadeoids were common in the lowlands. The insect-pollinated flowering plants, so common today, appeared first during the Triassic.

Little is known of the land fauna of Australia and Antarctica, but land animals seem to have been able to migrate between all other continents.

Triassic scene with browsing rhynchosaurs.

The Jurassic Period

(195 to 135 million years ago)

Most of the Jurassic deposits were laid down in the sea until near to the end of the period. The holostean fish were by now very numerous and varied and included deep-bodied forms such as *Dapedius*. The first of the teleosts had also evolved by the late Jurassic. The cartilaginous fish had by now recovered from the arrival of bony fish in the sea, and early sharks, rays and chimaeroids appeared.

A variety of reptiles preyed upon the diverse marine fauna. Ichthyosaurs reached the peak of their development in the Jurassic, including the swordfish-like *Eurhinosaurus*. Like them, the short-necked plesiosaurs were mainly fish eaters, but both groups were preyed upon by the large-headed, long-necked pliosaurs. The marine crocodiles provided yet another type of marine Jurassic reptile. All of these probably included cephalopods in their diet, for squid-like belemnoids and the shell-inhabiting ammonoids, up to 6 feet across, were common in Jurassic seas.

Marine life of the Jurassic

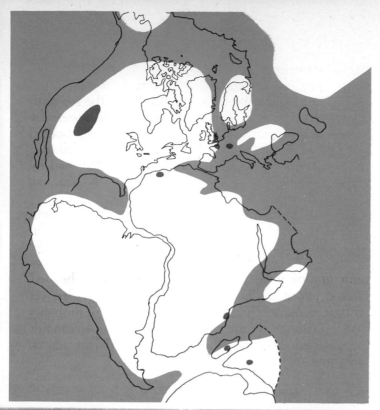

Jurassic terrestrial life

A small glimpse of Middle Jurassic life is provided by the Stonesfield Slate, quarried near Oxford in the nineteenth century. Together with a variety of other remains, both invertebrate and vertebrate, these rocks contain fragments of three different types of small early mammal, including the rodent-like multituberculates.

Apart from the Stonesfield Slate, our knowledge of Jurassic vertebrate life outside the seas comes from rocks laid down near the end of the period. The best-known fauna is that found in the western United States, in Wyoming and Colorado. These rocks of the Morrison Formation have provided several hundred tons of dinosaur bones, which occur in such profusion that early paleontologists found a herdsman's cabin partly constructed of fossil vertebrae, many belonging to the great sauropods, or to the large carnosaurs that preyed on them. Medium-sized coelurosaurs were also very common, and ornithischian dinosaurs included

Two scenes of Jurassic life on land with sauropods and stegosaurs.

small bipedal herbivores, as well as *Stegosaurus*.

A fauna similar to that of the United States is found at Tendaguru in East Africa. *Brachiosaurus* is found in both areas, and Tendaguru has other dinosaurs similar to *Diplodocus* and *Stegosaurus* of the Morrison Formation. Small mammal remains, too, were found in both continents. These areas were, however, isolated from Asia, because the Pacific and Tethys Oceans were united by a sea that covered much of Europe and northern Asia.

Remains of life in the air in Jurassic times include the specimens of the first bird, *Archaeopteryx*, showing even the impressions of the feathers, and many different kinds of flying pterosaurian reptiles, whose gliding membranes can be seen. Although Jurassic plant life was similar to that of the Triassic, Jurassic climates seem to have been milder. India may have become separate from the rest of Gondwanaland during the Jurassic—the first sign perhaps of the breaking-up of the super-continents.

First bird and pterosaurs

The Cretaceous Period
(135 to 70 million years ago)
Throughout this period the dinosaurs continued to dominate the land, and they are known from every continent. Although the fauna of the early Cretaceous is not very well known it seems to have been very similar to that of the late Jurassic. Large sauropods and carnosaurs were still common, though larger bipedal ornithischians such as *Iguanodon* had appeared.

This fauna was very different from that of the late Cretaceous. Large sauropods were rare, and the medium-sized coelurosaurs had been replaced by the ostrich-like ornithomimids. Such great carnosaurs as *Tyrannosaurus* must have fed mainly upon the varied herbivorous ornithischians, which included the duck-billed hadrosaurs and the armoured ankylosaurs and ceratopsians.

The appearance of these new types of herbivore was probably related to the great change in plant life that had taken place. The modern types of flowering plant became common some time in the middle of the Cretaceous. Hardwood trees slowly replaced the conifers as the dominant trees of the forests. These new plants provided fruit, flowers and

nectar as new sources of food, causing great changes in all life on land.

Vast areas of the continents were covered by the sea and the final break-up of the super-continents probably took place during the Cretaceous, and the Atlantic Ocean dates from this period. The presence of the new dinosaur groups of the Upper Cretaceous in both North America and Eurasia proves that some pathway must have existed between these continents even at the end of the period.

The dinosaur-dominated
Cretaceous world

Life in and above Cretaceous seas

Marine life of the Cretaceous

By the end of this period, the cartilaginous and the bony fish faunas were essentially very similar to those of today. Many of the living genera of shark, skate and ray had also already appeared, and the teleosts gradually replaced the holosteans as the dominant form of bony fish during the Cretaceous period.

Although the ichthyosaurs had become quite rare by the Upper Cretaceous, both the long-necked plesiosaurs such as *Elasmosaurus* and the large-headed pliosaurs such as *Kronosaurus* flourished until toward the end of the period. Several different groups of turtle took to a marine life during this time, as did several types of large lizard, such as *Tylosaurus*.

The remains of a great variety of sea-going vertebrates have been very well preserved in the Upper Cretaceous Niobrara Chalk deposits of Kansas in the United States. Among many others these included the giant pterosaur *Pteranodon* and the birds *Hesperornis* and *Ichthyornis*.

The Cenozoic Era

This last era covers the last 70 million years. It includes the Tertiary and Quaternary periods and only minor changes were needed to change the early Tertiary world into that of today. The Andes and Rocky Mountains had already appeared in the late Cretaceous, and early mammals are preserved in the sediments deposited as these eroded. The other major mountain systems, the Alps and Himalayas, rose in the later half of the Tertiary.

While achieving their present relationships to each other, the continents continued to move northward, and their climates to become cooler, culminating in the Ice Ages of the Quaternary.

The main faunal change is merely the story of competition within the mammals, as more archaic or conservative groups were replaced by their progressive cousins. These changes may have been accelerated by the increasing dominance of flowering herbaceous plants and grasses during the early Cenozoic, which provided a new element in the diet of the herbivores, and a new type of grassland environment.

149

The Lower Tertiary Period
(25 to 70 million years ago)

The Paleocene, Eocene and Oligocene epochs are included in the Lower Tertiary. At first, the only mammals similar to those alive today were the marsupial opossums, the little insectivores, and lemur-like primates. Many of the browsing herbivores that rapidly evolved were, like *Uintatherium* and *Arsinoitherium,* members of groups now extinct. Others bore little resemblance to their more advanced descendants of the later Tertiary.

Except in the mid-Eocene and late Oligocene, the faunas of North America and Eurasia were so similar in the Lower Tertiary that a connection between these continents must have existed, presumably via Alaska and Siberia across the Bering Strait. The presence of fossils of the warmth-loving crocodiles in the Eocene of Canada, suggests that these areas still lay further south than they do today.

South America was isolated for most of the Lower Tertiary. Only in the early Paleocene did a connection to North America allow early marsupials and primitive herbivorous

Lower Tertiary forest scene with early primate and Uintatherium

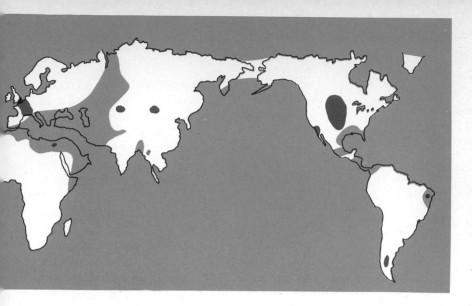

placentals into South America, and marsupials such as the borhyaenids and caenolestids took the place of the carnivorous placentals. The herbivores were derived from radiations of the primitive ungulates such as the litopterns, and of the edentates (armadillos, glyptodonts and ground sloths).

The Upper Tertiary Period
(2 to 25 million years ago)
This period includes the Miocene and Pliocene epochs and mammal faunas had become far more modern—75 to 80 percent of the known Upper Tertiary families are still alive today. This change is due to the extinction of the more archaic types of herbivore and to the fact that the artiodactyls were better adapted to feeding on the grasslands that displaced the lowland forests over wide areas.

Intermigration between North America and Eurasia began again in the Upper Miocene. The climate of the Bering region seems to have become cooler, for animals that live in more tropical climates did not pass through it. Only the rhinos and horses made this journey, together with the elephants that spread earlier from Africa to Eurasia.

Most of the Lower Tertiary mammals of South America continued into the Upper Tertiary with little change. Although little rodents and primates reached the continent from North America in the Mid-Tertiary, these probably

Upper Tertiary forest scene including

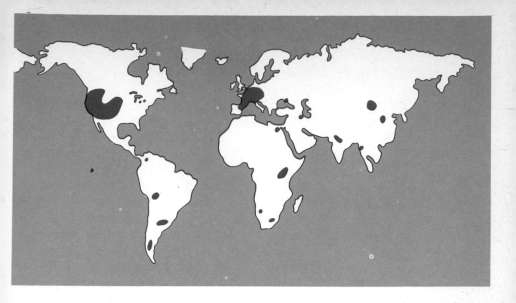

reached it along a chain of Central American islands. Only in the later Pliocene does the appearance of ground sloths and glyptodonts in North America prove that a continuous Panama land bridge had emerged by this time.

'giraffe' camels, dicerathere and shovel-tusker

The Quaternary Period
(The last 2 million years)
During the Pleistocene and Recent Epochs four Ice Ages, separated by warmer interglacial periods, covered the northern land areas. As the ice slowly advanced and retreated, so the climate zones and their mammal faunas moved across the continents. Many of the 'typical African' mammals of today such as the antelope, rhinoceros and hippopotamus arrived there in the Pleistocene, driven southward out of their European homelands.

Because millions of cubic miles of water formed continental ice sheets, the Pleistocene sea level sank until only Australia remained isolated. Such animals as bison, horses and mammoths crossed the Bering region between North America and Eurasia. While edentates and porcupines crossed the Panama Isthmus into North America, mastodont elephants and advanced carnivores and ungulates penetrated southward, causing the final extinction of the carnivorous marsupials and archaic ungulates of South America.

An unexplained feature of the Pleistocene was the appearance of giant representatives of nearly every order of mammals, from platypus, kangaroo and lemur, to deer, beaver, edentates and even unusually large elephants. All these giants disappeared during the Recent epoch and because this is not associated with any obvious climatic change, we must therefore suspect that man, who evolved during the Pleistocene period, may very possibly have played a large part in these extinctions.

The earth's mammal faunas have been even more reduced during the last hundred years, until many of the herbivores that once roamed North America and Africa in their thousands are nearly extinct or can be seen only in protected game parks. Skeletons, carefully excavated and mounted, are the closest we can come to the great Mesozoic dinosaurs. It will be a tragedy if inert bones and caged beasts are all that remain to whisper to our children of the beauty and dignity of the mammals with whom we now share this planet.

BOOKS TO READ

Evolution of the Vertebrates. E. H. Colbert. Wiley, 1955. A very readable survey of the subject.

Man and the Vertebrates. A. S. Romer. University of Chicago Press, 1941. A comprehensive study of vertebrate zoology, including fossil and recent forms.

Dinosaurs, their discovery and their world. E. H. Colbert. E. P. Dutton, 1961. A lively and complete discussion of everything pertaining to dinosaurs.

Life of the Past. G. G. Simpson, Yale University Press, 1953. A discussion of paleontologic principles.

Horses. G. G. Simpson. Oxford University Press, 1951. A comprehensive account of modern horses and the evolution of the groups.

The Succession of Life through Geological Time. K. P. Oakley and H. M. Muir-Wood, British Museum (Natural History), 1949. An excellent book on British fossils.

Prehistoric Animals. J. Angusta and Z. Burian. London: Spring Books, 1956. The colorplates are outstanding.

The Fossil Book. C. L. Fenton and M. A. Fenton. Doubleday, 1958. A comprehensive survey of invertebrate and vertebrate fossils with fine line drawings.

The Origin of Races. C. S. Coon. Knopf, 1962. An excitingly written and up to date account of human evolution.

PLACES TO VISIT

Extensive exhibits of fossil vertebrates can be seen at the following museums:

American Museum of Natural History, New York, N.Y.; United States National Museum, Washington, D.C.; Field Museum of Natural History, Chicago, Ill.; Peabody Museum of Natural History, Yale University. New Haven, Conn.; Museum of Comparative Zoology, Harvard University, Cambridge, Mass.; Carnegie Museum, Pittsburgh, Pa.; Milwaukee Public Museum, Milwaukee, Wisc.; Exhibit Museum of the University of Michigan, Ann Arbor, Mich.

Some other excellent but more regional exhibits of fossil vertebrates can be seen at:

New York State Museum, Education Building, Albany, N.Y.; Cleveland Museum of Natural History, Cleveland, Ohio; University of Kansas Natural History Museum, Lawrence, Kansas; South Dakota School of Mines Museum, Rapid City, S.D.; Museum of Northern Arizona, Flagstaff, Ariz.; Denver Museum of Natural History, Denver, Colo.; Los Angeles County Museum, Los Angeles, Calif.

Outstanding Canadian museums include:

National Museum, Ottawa; Royal Ontario Museum, Toronto.

INDEX

Page numbers in bold type refer to illustrations.

159

OTHER TITLES IN THE SERIES

The GROSSET ALL-COLOR GUIDES provide a library of authoritative information for readers of all ages. Each comprehensive text with its specially designed illustrations yields a unique insight into a particular area of man's interests and culture.

NOW AVAILABLE

Prehistoric Animals
Bird Behavior
Wild Cats
Fossil Man
Porcelain
Military Uniforms, 1686–1918
Birds of Prey
Flower Arranging
Microscopes & Microscopic
   Life
The Plant Kingdom
Rockets & Missiles
Flags of the World
Atomic Energy
Weather & Weather
   Forecasting
Trains
Sailing Ships & Sailing
   Craft
Electronics
Myths & Legends of
   Ancient Greece
Cats
Discovery of Africa
Horses & Ponies
Fishes of the World
Astronomy
Snakes of the World
Dogs

SOON TO BE PUBLISHED

Guns
Exploring the Planets
Discovery of The American
   West
Animals of Australia & New
   Zealand
Jewelry
Warships
Mammals of the World
Trees of the World
Computers at Work
Architecture
Monkeys & Apes
The Animal Kingdom
Discovery of North America
English Victoriana
Natural History Collecting
Myths & Legends of
   Ancient Egypt
The Human Body
Tropical Aquarium Fishes
African Animals
Polar Animals
Myths & Legends of the
   South Seas
Myths & Legends of Rome
Myths & Legends of India
Arms & Armor
Discovery of South America